PROBLEM SOLVING IN ENVIRONMENTAL BIOLOGY

A R Ennos & S E R Bailey

SCHOOL OF BIOLOGICAL SCIENCES,
UNIVERSITY OF MANCHESTER

Longman
Scientific &
Technical

Longman Scientific & Technical,
Longman Group Limited,
Longman House, Burnt Mill, Harlow,
Essex CM20 2JE, England
and Associated Companies, throughout the world

Copublished in the United States with
John Wiley & Sons, Inc., 605 Third Avenue, New York, NY 10158

First published 1995

British Library Cataloguing in Publication Data
A catalogue entry for this title is available from the British Library.

ISBN 0-582-21874-8

Library of Congress Cataloging-in-Publication Data
Ennos, A. R.
    Problem solving in environmental biology / A.R. Ennos and S.E.R.
Bailey.
        p.   cm.
    Includes bibliographical references (p.   ) and index.
    ISBN 0-470-23489-X (Wiley)
    1. Environmental sciences.   2. Environmental sciences—Problems,
exercises, etc.   3. Ecology.   4. Ecology—Problems, exercises, etc.
I. Bailey, S. E. R.   II. Title.
GE140.E53   1995
628—dc20   95-4997
                                                                  CIP

Set by 6 in 10 on 12pt Bembo
Printed in Malaysia

CONTENTS

Contents

ACKNOWLEDGEMENTS

Some of the problems in this book are derived from finals problem papers set by the universities of Manchester and York. We would like to thank the following people for their permission to use problems that they devised for these exams: Dr Mike Earnshaw for problem 2.2; Prof. M. J. Usher for problem 2.3; Prof. John Lawton for problems 2.4 and 2.5; Dr John Tallis for problems 4.1 and 5.2; Dr Mike Hounsome for problem 5.4; Dr Richard Law for problem 5.5; and Dr Lawrence Cook for problem 7.5. We also thank the following for permission to use unpublished data as a basis for problems: Ms Emma Sellars for example 1.7; Ms Hazel Norman for problem 3.2; Dr Derek Yalden for problem 4.2 and Prof. Ian Douglas for problem 5.1.

We are indebted to the following for permission to reproduce copyright material: Blackwell Science Ltd for our figures 7.2, 7.3, 7.4 and 7.5; Nuclear Electric for material associated with Heysham Nature Reserve.

Whilst every effort has been made to trace the owners of copyright material, in a few cases this has proved impossible and we take this opportunity to offer our apologies to any copyright holders whose rights we may unwittingly have infringed.

PREFACE: Why we wrote this book

We wrote this book for three reasons: because we needed to work up some examples for a set of undergraduate seminars, because someone suggested we put the examples together into a book, and because some other biologists said that they would find such a book useful in their classes. What we have not done is to write a primer textbook of ecology or environmental management – there are many good books on this subject already. But we did recognise that there was a need to develop an organised framework to train undergraduate students to apply their theoretical and practical skills to solve real-life problems.

The importance of these skills is recognised in most undergraduate courses, as the widespread use of a 'problem-solving' examination demonstrates. However, these examinations are often heavily biased towards mathematical problems, especially statistical ones, and tend to ignore the problems of the real world. We wanted to produce a much wider range of problems, many of which are based on real data. We also wanted to show that there are common elements in the process of solving problems which superficially seem to be unrelated. This should help students to identify parallels between novel problems and ones they have already tackled: boosting their confidence and helping them avoid the feelings of panic which the sight of numerical problems so commonly engenders.

The book should also help to reinforce basic concepts which are covered in traditional course units, such as population ecology, pollution ecology and conservation. Its eight chapters are divided between four sections. The first section categorises the types of problems that may be encountered, and describes the skills which will help to find the solution. The second section deals with natural ecosystems and environmental resources. This provides a sound base for understanding the third section, on human impacts, and the fourth section, which deals with devising programmes to manage the environment and cope with the impacts.

Within each chapter, a range of problems are set which not only can be used for tutorials and problem-solving classes but which also illustrate many of the underlying principles of environmental biology. The book may therefore be used in conjunction with traditional courses in environmental biology both to encourage active learning and to assess students' understanding. For this reason, reference is made in each problem to chapters in one or more standard textbooks or research papers. These can provide the interested student with a wider backgound to the scientific basis of the problem than can be given here and may present the results of other studies.

The annotated solutions to each of the problems are presented at the end of each chapter, so that the student can attempt the solutions before turning to the answers.

A GENERAL APPROACH TO PROBLEM SOLVING

1 INTRODUCTION AND BASIC SKILLS

Introduction

All of us solve problems every day. One purpose of this book is to show that the types of problems we tackle in our professional lives as environmental biologists are similar to these everyday problems, and may be solved in the same way. In both cases we must combine our knowledge of how the world works with details of the particular case in hand. Most people, for instance, can combine their knowledge of how stoves work and their skill in cooking to make a meal using the ingredients they have in their fridge. The difference is only one of scale; you need more specialised knowledge and a wider range of skills to solve problems in environmental biology.

Because of the range of expertise you need it is all too easy to become intimidated by a problem in an area about which you feel you know very little. There is no need to panic, however; problems which on the surface look complicated can prove to be fairly simple on closer inspection and you may not need to know all the details, just as you do not need to know about food science to cook. You might also find that you have more background knowledge tucked away in your memory than you realise. One aim of this book is to improve your feel for the sort of information an environmental biologist requires and how it can be used. You can use information you have obtained from all sorts of sources: not just lectures on biology. You may be able to use scraps of information you remember from other academic subjects, such as chemistry, geography, physics and maths, or from books, magazines or television programmes. The important thing is to realise that information should not be compartmentalised; all's fair in love, war and problem solving.

Furthermore, just as there are common elements in the ways in which we solve everyday problems, it is also possible to identify a few common skills which can help us solve the more complex problems met by working environmental biologists. We have identified eight main skills which we think will help you to answer problems in this area.

Further reading

Bransford and Stein (1984).

Handling numbers and units

Units, formulae and conversions

Because the natural world is so variable and because it is so hard to make accurate measurements in the field, problems in environmental biology are rarely as clear-cut as those in physics, chemistry or mathematics and there is seldom a single right answer to a problem. Biologists seldom, if ever, need to perform complex mathematical analysis, so few of the problems given here require you to use much more than simple addition, subtraction, multiplication and division. Nevertheless, environmental biology *is* an empirical science and you must be able to manipulate numbers. As an environmental biologist (like any scientist), you must also be precise about the units with which you are working, which must conform to the SI (Système International d'Unités) system. The basic units are as follows:

Mass	Kilogram (kg)
Length	Metre (m)
Time	Second (s)

You should give answers to problems in these units, or in units derived from them. Volume, for instance, should be given in m^3 and speed in $m\ s^{-1}$, while density should be expressed as $kg\ m^{-3}$.

Example 1 A sample of contaminated topsoil 40 cm long by 30 cm wide by 20 cm deep cut from a factory site has a mass of 34.3 kg. Calculate its density.

Solution The density is the mass of soil (in kilograms) divided by its volume (in cubic metres):

$$\text{Density} = \frac{34.3}{0.40 \times 0.30 \times 0.20}$$

$$= 1429\ kg\ m^{-3}$$

$$= 1.4 \times 10^3\ kg\ m^{-3}.$$

Note that the final answer is given to only *two* significant figures. This is because it was calculated from data (the dimensions of the soil sample) which themselves were only determined to this degree of accuracy. An answer should always be presented to the same accuracy as that of the *least* accurate data item from which it was calculated.

You may also need to convert between different units and to remember or be able to look up important physical and chemical constants and several mathematical formulae. Table 1.1 is a list (by no means exhaustive) of information with which you should be familiar.

Logarithms One important skill that many students find particularly difficult is the use and interpretation of logarithms. Logarithms have been derived so that if numbers have a constant *ratio* between them, their logarithms will differ by a constant *amount*. Hence, the numbers 1, 10 and 100, which differ by ratios of 10, have logarithms to the base 10 ($\log_{10}$) of 0, 1 and 2, which differ by 1 each time.

The logarithm of 1 is always 0, but logarithms may have different 'bases'. In logarithms which have a base of 10 ($\log_{10}$), numbers differing by a ratio of 10 have logs which differ by 1. However, in 'natural logarithms' ($\log_e$ or ln) it is numbers which differ by the ratio 2.718 which have logs which differ by 1. In this book we

Table 1.1. Useful conversion factors, constants and formulae.	**Conversion factors** 1 hectare (ha) $= 10^4 \, m^2 = 100 \, m \times 100 \, m = 2.5$ acres 1 litre (l) $= 10^{-3} \, m^3 = 10 \, cm \times 10 \, cm \times 10 \, cm = 1.75$ pints 1 millilitre (ml) $= 10^{-6} \, m^3 = 1 \, cm^3$ 1 tonne (t) $= 10^3 \, kg$

Physical constants

Density of water $= 1000 \, kg \, m^{-3}$
Density of air $= 1.2 \, kg \, m^{-3}$
Specific heat of water $= 4.2 \times 10^3 \, J \, kg^{-1} \, °C^{-1}$

Chemical constants

1 mole $= 6 \times 10^{23}$ particles
Mass of 1 mole = relative molecular mass of substance (grams)
Volume of 1 mole of gas $= 24 \, l = 2.4 \times 10^{-2} \, m^3$
  (at room temperature and pressure)
1 molar solution (1 M) $= 1$ mole $l^{-1} = 1000$ moles m^{-3}
1 normal solution (1 N) $= 1$ mole $l^{-1} = 1000$ moles m^{-3} of ions
pH $= -\log_{10} [H^+]$
Composition of air = 80% nitrogen, 20% oxygen, 0.04% carbon dioxide

Formulae

$\pi = 3.14$
Area of a circle of radius $R = \pi R^2$
Volume of a sphere of radius $R = \frac{4}{3}\pi R^3$
Surface area of a sphere of radius $R = 4\pi R^2$
Volume of a cylinder of radius R and height $H = \pi R^2 H$
Volume of a cone of radius R and height $H = \frac{1}{3}\pi R^2 H$
Logarithms: of $\log AB^x = \log A + x(\log B)$
$\log_e x = 2.30 \log_{10} x$

usually use $\log_{10}$. Most scientific calculators have buttons to determine logarithms: simply press the log or ln buttons. To convert logs back to real numbers simply press the 10^x (for $\log_{10}$) or e^x (for $\log_e$) buttons.

One of the most important properties of logarithms is that they allow very different quantities to be compared and plotted on the same graph. For instance, if you plot the relationship between the number of tree species in woods of areas 100, 1000, 10 000, 100 000 and 1 000 000 m^2 (Fig. 1.1) most of the points are hopelessly congested at the left of the plot. By plotting species number against $\log_{10}$ area (Fig. 1.2) the data are spaced out evenly. Similarly, the concentration of chemical solutions can vary enormously and to overcome this problem logarithms have been used. The measure of acidity, pH, is actually given by the formula

$$pH = -\log_{10}[H^+]$$

where $[H^+]$ is the hydrogen ion concentration in moles per litre. Hence a solution containing 10^{-5} moles (mol) of hydrogen ions per litre will have a pH of 5.

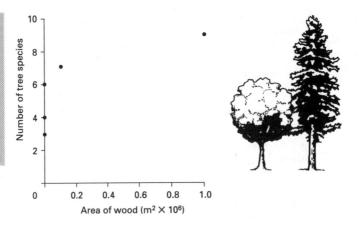

Figure 1.1. Graph showing the relationship between the size of woods and the numbers of species of tree they contain. The points are hopelessly congested towards the left of the plot.

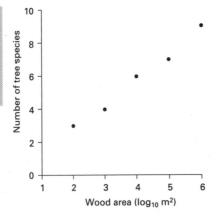

Figure 1.2. Plot of the number of species against $\log_{10}$ of the area of each wood. This log plot spreads the data out more evenly.

Ball parking   In many instances in your working life as an environmental biologist, you may not have hard data to hand and must perform rapid calculations to produce a quick 'ball park' answer. Such calculations may be required, for instance, to determine the approximate cost of materials to fence a nature reserve or the amount of wild flower seed to order. To perform these calculations you will need to know, or be able to look up, other relevant data (such as the approximate size of the nature reserve and the seeding rate). Just as in cooking without scales the ability to estimate quantities is an invaluable skill.

Example 2   Elephants are the most practical means of transport through the Indian rainforest because of the rough terrain, their only disadvantage being their weight. A scientific expedition needs to cross a bridge with a weight limit of 10 tonnes (t), in order to enter a nature reserve. Will their elephants be able to cross this bridge safely?

Solution You are unlikely, in the rainforest, to be able to look up or measure the weight of an elephant, but most people have some idea of just how big they are. Since the mass of an object is equal to volume times density the first thing to calculate is the volume. What is the volume of an elephant? Well, elephants are around 2–3 m long and have a (very roughly) cylindrical body of diameter, say, 1.5 m (and therefore radius of 0.75 m). The volume of a cylinder is given by $V = \pi R^2 H$, so with these figures the volume of the elephant is approximately

$$V = \pi \times 0.75^2 \times 2 \text{ up to } \pi \times 0.75^2 \times 3$$
$$= 3.53 \text{ to } 5.30 \text{ m}^3$$

The volume of the legs, trunk, etc. are very much less and can be ignored in this rough calculation. So what is the density of an elephant? Well, elephants (like us) can just about float in water and certainly swim, so they must have about the same density as water, 1000 kg m^{-3}. The approximate mass of the elephant is therefore

$$\text{Mass} = 1000 \times (3.5 \text{ to } 5.3)$$
$$= 3530 \text{ to } 5300 \text{ kg}$$

Note, however, that the length of the beast was estimated to only one significant figure so the weight should also be estimated to this low degree of accuracy. The weight of the elephant will be 4–5 $\times$ 10^3 kg or 4–5 t (textbook figures for weights of elephants range from 3 to 7 t).

The bridge should easily be able to withstand the weight of an elephant.

Note that this calculation would not have been accurate enough to determine whether our elephant could cross a bridge with weight limit of 4.5 t. It would have been necessary to devise a method of weighing it. This example shows up an important feature of problem solving, that different levels of accuracy are required to solve different problems.

Data handling In many problems, numerical data are presented either as figures or as graphs. You are then required to use your biological knowledge to calculate or infer other data.

Example 3 The river Almopeos in northern Greece is subjected to seasonal pollution by fruit canning factories which operate from 15 June to 10 September each year. A survey was carried out in 1992 to investigate the flow of water and levels of inorganic pollution at a point downstream from these factories before and during their operation. Results for discharge rate and nitrate concentrations on two separate occasions are given below:

Date	Discharge ($m^3 s^{-1}$)	Nitrate concentration ($mg\ l^{-1}$)
11 June	5.3	0.24
9 August	2.2	0.83

Calculate how much nitrate is flowing down the river on each occasion. Which value is higher and why?

Solution The amount of nitrate flowing downstream is equal to its concentration multiplied by the amount of water flowing downstream:

$$\text{Mass flux} = \text{Discharge} \times \text{nitrate concentration}$$

However, the units must be consistent, so nitrogen concentration must first be converted to kilograms per cubic metre. There are $1000\ l$ in a cubic metre and $10^6\ mg$ in a kilogram, so the nitrate concentration on 11 June is $240\ mg\ m^{-3}$ ($\times 1000$) which equals $2.4 \times 10^{-4}\ kg\ m^{-3}$ ($\div 10^6$). The mass flux on 11 June is therefore

$$5.3 \times 2.4 \times 10^{-4} = 1.3 \times 10^{-3}\ kg\ s^{-1} \quad \text{or} \quad 1.3\ g\ s^{-1}$$

The mass flux on 9 August is similarly

$$2.2 \times 8.3 \times 10^{-4} = 1.8 \times 10^{-3}\ kg\ s^{-1} \quad \text{or} \quad 1.8\ g\ s^{-1}$$

The latter value is higher and this may be due to the pollution produced by the canning factories.

Pattern recognition The ability to recognise biologically significant trends in a data set is a very important skill for a professional biologist. The ratio of $3:1$ cropping up in a particular character in the offspring of identical adults, for instance, tells a geneticist that the character is determined by a single allele and that the parents are both heterozygous at that allele. Similarly, differences in the preferred habitat of intertidal limpets are signalled by differences in their peak abundance up a rocky shore. Many problems involve the ability to recognise such patterns. Information may be provided in the form of tables or graphs, but even if data are given in tables it is a good idea to plot them as a graph. It is then much easier to spot trends and to identify such important features as peaks, asymptotes or thresholds.

Example 4 A number of *Paramecium aurelia* were placed in a growing tube and provided with a constant supply of food. The population density was then monitored over a 10-day

Time (days)	Population density (mm^{-3})
0	4.2 ± 0.42
1	7.3 ± 0.59
2	12.5 ± 0.87
3	20.2 ± 1.13
4	36.2 ± 2.03
5	61.3 ± 3.87
6	101.3 ± 5.78
7	167.3 ± 6.34
8	187.6 ± 8.43
9	191.2 ± 9.33
10	189.3 ± 10.41

Table 1.2. Population density of *P. aurelia* over a 10-day period.

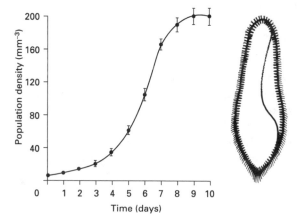

Figure 1.3. The population density of *P. aurelia* over a 10-day period.

period and the results (mean and standard error from sixteen samples) are given in Table 1.2. What do these results tell you about the population dynamics of this species?

Solution The first thing to do is to plot the data (Fig. 1.3). At first glance we can see that the population rises increasingly fast for the first 7 days, before levelling off. This looks like the typical exponential growth in population of a species which then reaches its carrying capacity, in this case at around 190 individuals mm^{-3}. This graph shows the population growth well, but it is hard to get any further meaning from a graph showing a curve. To determine whether it is indeed exponential growth, and if so the time it takes for the population to double, it is best to produce a plot of $\log_{10}$ (number) vs time (Fig. 1.4). If the growth is exponential this should produce a straight line. This plot gives a straight line, showing that growth is indeed exponential. The line of best fit between the data points has a slope of 0.23. Therefore for the population to double (i.e. for the $\log_{10}$ of the population to increase by 0.30, which is $\log_{10}$ of 2) will take $0.30/0.23 = 1.3$ days.

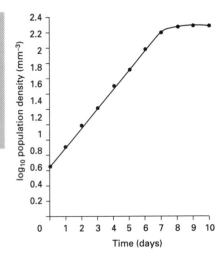

Figure 1.4. Plot of $\log_{10}$(population density) of *P. aurelia* against time. This plot produces a straight line, the slope of which is 0.23. The population of *P. aurelia* doubles every 1.3 days.

Data selection

Although in many problems you are given only the data which are necessary to work out particular answers, this is rather unrealistic. Working biologists are more usually presented with a large mass of information, only a fraction of which is relevant to the problem which has to be solved. This is largely because field workers understandably tend to measure as many parameters as possible and as often as they can 'just in case' the extra information proves useful. Some problems, therefore, contain information which is of no use in solving the problem and you must learn which data to select.

Example 5 One thousand *P. aurelia* were placed in a growing tube of volume 1000 mm^3 similar to the one used in the previous example. You already know that the population of this species under these conditions should double every 1.3 days, and it has a carrying capacity of 190 mm^{-3}. Estimate the population after 20 days.

Solution After 20 days the population should have easily reached its carrying capacity so its population will equal the maximum density (190 mm^{-3}) multiplied by the volume (1000 mm^3), which is 1.9×10^5.

The rate of population growth was irrelevant because at that rate of growth the initial population should double around fifteen times. The original population would be increased by a factor of 2^{15}, or over $30\,000$ times. The end population would be over 3×10^7, 150 times the carrying capacity.

Interpreting statistical information

Because of the variability of the natural world, environmental biologists must be able to interpret and use statistical information. This book does not set out to be a statistical text, but there are several basic aspects of statistics that must be emphasised.

First, no useful information can be gleaned from single measurements. For instance, if we have scales and we want to know how much bull elephants weigh, it is no use just weighing one animal. We have no idea how characteristic the animal is. The ultimate answer would be to measure *all* organisms in a population but this may be impractical and undesirable: it would take far too much time to locate and catch all bull elephants; and sampling may help to destroy the population which is being measured. Instead, fairly reliable information may be found by appropriate *random* sampling of a small fraction of the population. In the case of bull elephants we might decide to weigh sixteen animals. The results from these measurements can be used to determine the following statistics:

> Weights of bull elephants (t): 4.5, 5.2, 4.9, 4.3, 4.6, 4.8, 4.6, 4.9, 4.5, 5.0, 4.8, 4.6, 4.6, 4.7, 4.5, 4.7

The **sample mean** (in this case the average weight) is our best estimate for the population mean (the average weight of bull elephants). The sample mean is found by adding the data values together and dividing by the number of values. In this case the mean is $75.2/16 = 4.70$ t to three significant figures.

The **sample standard deviation** gives an indication of how variable the population is. In this case it would show how much, on average, we would expect the weight of an elephant picked at random to differ from the mean (either lighter or heavier). The higher the standard deviation is, therefore, the more varied the population. Standard deviation is found using a rather complicated mathematical expression. However, most calculators are nowadays equipped with a button (σ_{n-1}) which automatically works it out for you. In this case the estimated population standard deviation $= 0.22$. If, as often happens in biology, the mass of the population varies according to the normal distribution (in which animals with a mass nearer the mean are more common than those with a mass further from the mean) then we would expect 95 per cent of the elephants to weigh within about two standard deviations of the sample mean. In this case 95 per cent of elephants should weigh between about 4.26 and 5.14 t.

If we had taken a sample of sixteen different elephants, the mean mass we calculated would have been different. The **standard error of the mean** is a measure of the variability we can expect in the means we calculate. It is equal to the standard deviation divided by the square root of the number of observations. The larger the sample we take, therefore, the smaller the standard error. In this case the more elephants we sample the less effect unusually large or small elephants would have on the mean we calculated. For this sample the standard error $= 0.22/4 = 0.055$ (standard errors are usually given to one more decimal place than the mean). Just as we could say that 95 per cent of the elephants would be between 4.26 and 5.14 t we can calculate **confidence intervals** for the mean of the population. We can be 95 per cent confident that the population mean is within about two standard errors of the sample mean. In this case the mean should be between 4.59 and 4.81 t.

Note that if we take a larger sample we can produce a better estimate of the population mean. However, it would take a lot more work. To halve the standard error would involve quadrupling the sample size (and presumably the amount of work). Sampling must therefore inevitably involve compromise. A good environmental biologist will know when to stop working! For instance, after only sixteen measurements we can be pretty sure that the mean mass of bull elephants is more than 4.5 t. If that is all we have tried to show we can stop there.

In many cases environmental biologists want to determine whether one group of organisms is different from another, or whether one or more treatments have a significant effect. In this case it is necessary to work out population statistics for each group. For instance, if we are interested in whether female elephants are lighter than males we should also sample the females. We might come up with the following results:

Weights of female elephants (t) = 4.3, 4.6, 4.5, 4.4, 4.7, 4.1, 4.5, 4.4, 4.2, 4.3, 4.5, 4.4, 4.5, 4.4, 4.3, 4.3

Mean mass = 4.40 t
Standard deviation = 0.15 t
Standard error of the mean = 0.038 t

There is clearly some overlap – some females are bigger than some males – but on average males seem to be heavier. To determine whether there is a significant difference between males and females it is a good idea to draw the data on a graph with standard error bars around each mean (Fig. 1.5). Inspection of this graph can tell you rapidly whether there are likely to be significant differences; if the error bars overlap the populations are unlikely to differ significantly: if they do not, we can be about 95 per cent confident that they differ. To determine the exact level of significance (which is not required in the problems in this book) you could carry out either a t-test, or, if there are more than two populations, analysis of variance (ANOVA). You can look up how to do both these tests in Watt (1993). In this case there seems to be no overlap between the standard error bars of male and female elephants; we have shown that males are significantly heavier than females.

In many cases, environmental biologists do not measure quantitative data about an organism. Instead they count the numbers of organisms which fit into different **categories**. For instance, in a survey of elephants you might count the numbers of male and female elephants with and without tusks. The data would look something like Table 1.3. It is not possible to work out means and standard errors for this data, yet it is still possible to determine whether tusks are significantly more common in one

Figure 1.5. Mean plus and minus standard error of the masses of male and female elephants. There is no overlap of the error bars, suggesting that there may be a significant difference between the sexes.

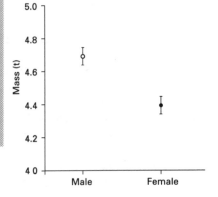

	Presence of tusks		
Sex	With	Without	Total
Male	18 (10)	12 (20)	30
Female	12 (20)	48 (40)	60
Total	30	60	90

Table 1.3. The numbers of male and female elephants with or without tusks. Observed values are given in bold type, expected values (those we would expect if tusks were randomly distributed between the sexes) are in brackets.

of the sexes. The first step is to calculate a **contingency table** for the number of elephants you would expect in each category if tusks were randomly distributed between the sexes. For instance, since a third of the animals caught (30) were male and one third of all animals (30) have tusks, you would expect one ninth (10) to be males with tusks. The general expression for the expected numbers in row A, column B is given by the expression

$$N_{A,B} = \frac{\text{Sum of organisms in row A} \times \text{sum of organisms in column B}}{\text{Total number of organisms}}$$

Table 1.3 shows the finished contingency table. We can see that in fact more males have tusks than we would have expected and fewer females. To determine whether this is a significant difference or whether you chose more tusked males by chance, we must calculate the value of Chi-squared, which is given by the following expression:

$$\text{Chi-squared} = \sum \left[\frac{(O - E)^2}{E} \right]$$

where O is the observed number and E the expected number for each state. All the values are added together (Σ) to give the final value for Chi-squared. In this case

$$\text{chi-squared} = (18 - 10)^2/10 + (12 - 20)^2/20 + (12 - 20)^2/20 + (48 - 40)^2/40$$

$$\text{chi-squared} = 64/10 + 64/20 + 64/20 + 64/40 = 14.4$$

There is a significant difference if chi-squared is greater than a value which can be looked up in statistical tables. In this case, with one degree of freedom (the number of degrees of freedom is given by the expression $(N - 1) \times (M - 1)$, where N is the number of rows and M the number of columns), chi-squared must exceed 3.84. This is clearly true, so we can say with some confidence that male elephants develop tusks more frequently than the females.

Further reading

Watt (1993), Cadogan and Sutton (1994).

Example 6　An experimental investigation was carried out into the effect of spraying a crop of winter wheat, *Triticum aestivum*, with chlormequat chloride (CCC) growth regulator on the incidence of lodging (falling over). Wheat was grown in eight randomised blocks, of which four were subjected to the treatment with CCC and four left untreated. In July, just before harvest, the investigator recorded the total percentage of wheat in each treatment which had lodged: 15 per cent of treated plants had lodged compared with 32 per cent of untreated. Does this represent a significant difference? How might the experiment have been improved?

Solution   With such large differences in the incidence of lodging between treatments it seems likely that there was an effect. However, it is impossible to carry out meaningful statistical analysis on the results which were collected. The two treatments cannot be compared using a *t*-test or analysis of variance because the investigator has only collected *one* value for the incidence of lodging for each treatment. There is therefore no way of determining the magnitude of the variation within each treatment and no way of telling whether the two treatments are significantly different. Neither is it possible to carry out a chi-squared test, because the investigator did not determine the actual *numbers* of plants which had lodged or stood up, only the percentages.

The experiment might have been improved in one of two ways. The best way would be to record the incidence of lodging of each of the plots separately. This would have given four values for each treatment which could have been used to calculate the amount of variation within the crop. Statistical testing would therefore have been possible using a *t*-test or analysis of variance. Alternatively the investigator could have actually counted the numbers of plants lodged and upright. However, this would be very time consuming and might be misleading since plants do not fall over on their own but in blocks. This example illustrates the importance of replication in field trials.

Design of a programme of investigation

Problems in which data are examined or manipulated are all to some extent artificial because as a working biologist you will have to collect your own data and indeed to decide which data to collect. Some problems will therefore call on you to design experiments or programmes of investigation. In these cases it is vital to follow the rules of experimental science, including adequate controls in the design and explaining how the data might be analysed statistically.

Further reading

Barnard, Gilbert and McGregor (1993).

Example 7   Design an experiment to test the relative effects of applying four different amounts of nitrogen fertiliser, 0, 3.5, 7 and 14 g of nitrogen per square metre per year in 25 fortnightly applications (researchers get a fortnight off at Christmas) on to calcareous grassland at Wardlaw, Derbyshire. The field site is split into sixteen plots each of dimensions 1 × 1 m in an 8 × 2 m grid. You are supplied with a quantity of 20 mM ammonium nitrate solution fertiliser.

Solution The first thing to do is to arrange for replication in your experiment. Each treatment should be given to four plots. Next you must decide how to arrange the treatments around the plots. It is essential to randomise the design to control for any differences within the plot. You could randomise totally, arranging treatments randomly in each of the sixteen blocks. However, in this case one treatment might tend to be restricted to one end of the site. A better solution would be to split the site into four main 'blocks' of 2×2 m and randomise each of the four treatments within each block.

Next, you must decide how much fertiliser you must add to each plot. A litre of 1 M ammonium nitrate will contain 1 mole of the substance. The formula of ammonium nitrate is NH_4NO_3, so this will contain 2 moles of nitrogen, a mass of 28 g (the atomic weight of nitrogen is 14). Therefore 1 litre of 20 mM ammonium nitrate will contain $28 \times 0.020 = 0.56$ g of nitrogen. To supply 14 g of nitrogen each square metre must be given $14/0.56 = 25$ l of fertiliser. Each plot is $1 \times 1 = 1$ m^2 so must be given $25 \times 1 = 25$ l fertiliser per year. This must be spread over 25 applications, however, so $25/25 = 1$ l must be applied to each plot at each visit.

What about the other plots? You could apply 0.5, 0.25 and 0 l of fertiliser to get the correct rates of 7, 3.5 and 0 g nitrogen per year. However, you would be adding different quantities of water to each treatment, which might itself have an effect. To control for this the same amount of water should be added to each plot. The best way to do this is to add 1 l of fertiliser diluted by a factor of 2 and 4 respectively to produce the 7 and 3.5 g nitrogen plots and 1 l of water to each zero nitrogen plot.

Deciding between conflicting interests

Conflicting interests frequently arise during the management of a site or industrial plant. As a biologist you will often have to work as part of a team with economists, engineers and planners to decide what must be done. You must therefore be aware of other pressures, both financial and social, which may mean that the best solution for wildlife cannot be taken. To tackle this sort of problem you should list the relevant factors and then go on to make and justify your decision for a certain course of action.

Example 8 A small area of oak/hornbeam woodland with an understorey of hazel situated near the edge of a large industrial town has been bought by the council, who want it to provide recreation for the public and to be a useful conservation area. What conflicts arise between management for these two aims and how would you manage the woods?

Solution To produce a good amenity wood you must first supply open areas for picnicking and also a range of nature trails for the public to follow. The easiest and pleasantest woods to walk through are those with many large trees forming a dense canopy. These restrict the penetration of light and limit growth of an understorey so that there is a low diversity of both flora and fauna. Dead trees are also best removed to keep the wood tidy and prevent accidents. This reduces the number of detritivores in the wood. Diversity will be restricted largely to the top of the canopy and to the vegetation growing around the edge of clearings.

Coppiced woodland. Frequent cutting allows the development of ground vegetation, including many perennial herbs. A mosaic of coppice cut in different years produces a range of habitats, with high diversity of invertebrates and birds.

To produce a good wildlife conservation zone, in contrast, the wood should be subjected to more intense 'coppice' management, cutting down trees and other vegetation (apart from a few 'standard' trees) in a small area every few years to open up the canopy and allow growth of herbaceous plants and shrubs. This management will produce a patchwork of areas which have recovered to different extents from disturbance and which will provide habitats for a wide variety of species of invertebrates, birds and mammals. Dead trees may be left to rot. However, many of the areas will seem scruffy and overgrown to the public and may be impenetrable.

To overcome these conflicts of interest it may be best to split the wood up and manage areas nearest the car park for amenity and those further away for conservation value. However, the wood could be managed almost entirely as a coppice, though more effort would have to be put into interpreting the different age areas.

Further reading

Green (1981: Ch. 7).

Communicating your answer

However good you are at solving problems, this is no use if you cannot communicate your answers so that people can understand both what you have done and why. Always include your reasoning and mathematical working in your answers to problems. It is also very important to be able to describe biological processes and effects in simple, straightforward English, without abbreviations or jargon. Environmental biologists have to deal with, and try to influence, both industrialists and the general public. If you cannot communicate your ideas to them in a straightforward way this not only means that they will not understand what you are saying but that you yourself probably do not fully understand either! Your explanation should always be comprehensible to a relatively intelligent non-specialist. You could try out your answers on a fellow student who is studying another subject.

NATURAL ECOSYSTEMS AND RESOURCES

ADAPTATION, BEHAVIOUR AND EVOLUTION

Seasonal acclimation in molluscs

Background Different animals respond in different ways to changes in temperature. In mammals, birds and some flying insects, the body temperature is kept at a constant high value by a combination of internal heat production and physiological and behavioural modifications (endothermic homoiothermy). Many reptiles keep a constant high temperature by behavioural means such as basking in the sun (exothermic homoiothermy). In contrast, many invertebrates conform passively to the environmental temperature (poikilothermy). However, they frequently show acclimatisation to maintain their rates of activity, growth and metabolism, making compensatory changes in response to the temperatures encountered in different latitudes, seasons and altitudes.

A typical seasonal temperature acclimation is shown by the heart rate of *Acmaea limatula*, a marine intertidal limpet in the Northern Hemisphere (Fig. 2.1). The graphs are curved, but by plotting logarithm of heart rate, the graphs become straight lines: it is easier to fit a straight line rather than a curve to data points, and easier to read interpolated values. Note the following:

1. In both seasons, the heart rate is sensitive to the environmental temperature, and the sensitivity has not altered greatly (the slopes are similar). The sensitivity can be quantified by the temperature coefficient or Q_{10}. This is the factor by which a reaction velocity is increased for a rise of $10\,°C$. For example, late summer limpets show an increase in heart rate from 21 to 58 beats per minute when the temperature rises $10\,°C$ from 9 to $19\,°C$: the Q_{10} is therefore 58/21 which is 2.8.

2. Throughout the range of environmental temperatures, the heart rate is higher in late winter than in late summer. These differences are probably significant statistically, because the standard error ranges about the means do not overlap.

3. The vertical distance between the curves is a measure of the degree of temperature compensation. Most invertebrates show this kind of temperature acclimation, although the compensation may be only partial rather than complete. There are also a few instances in which no compensation and even reverse acclimation occur.

4. By the end of winter, after acclimation to a sea temperature of $14\,°C$, the heart rate at $14\,°C$ is almost identical to the heart rate at $20\,°C$ of the same animals measured at the end of summer, after acclimation to a sea temperature of $20\,°C$. Thus the limpets have shown almost complete compensation, and are as active in winter as in summer.

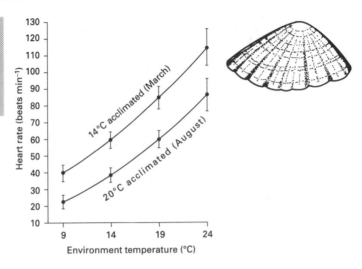

Figure 2.1. Heart rates at different environmental temperatures in limpets *Acmaea* recorded at two different seasons.

Further reading

Begon *et al.* (1986: Ch. 2), Hochachka and Somero (1973), Schmidt-Nielson (1990).

Data and questions

Using the above information as background, you are asked to interpret the results of two experiments in which the heart rates of two species of land snail have been measured at different environmental temperatures before and after the snails have

Snails in hibernation.

Table 2.1. Mean heart rates of eight *Helix aspersa* in late autumn, immediately before and 13 days after inducing hibernation by transferring from 20 °C to 5 °C.	Temperature (°C)	Acclimated to 20 °C			Acclimated to 5 °C		
		Mean	Standard error	Log$_{10}$ mean	Mean	Standard error	Log$_{10}$ mean
	6	13.3	0.9	1.12	8.8	0.5	0.94
	10	15.9	1.0	1.20	11.4	0.5	1.06
	14	19.2	1.4	1.28	14.8	0.6	1.17
	18	23.2	2.1	1.37	19.3	0.9	1.29
	22	28.1	3.0	1.45	25.3	1.4	1.40
	26	33.9	4.5	1.53	33.7	2.1	1.53

Table 2.2. Mean heart rates of six *Helix lucorum* in late autumn, immediately before and 13 days after inducing hibernation by transferring from 20 °C to 5 °C.	Temperature (°C)	Acclimated to 20 °C			Acclimated to 5 °C		
		Mean	Standard error	Log$_{10}$ mean	Mean	Standard error	Log$_{10}$ mean
	6	10.2	0.2	1.01	6.5	0.7	0.81
	10	13.2	0.4	1.12	8.8	0.9	0.94
	14	17.2	0.8	1.23	12.1	1.2	1.08
	18	22.5	1.5	1.35	16.5	1.8	1.22
	22	29.5	2.6	1.47	22.7	2.5	1.36
	26	38.6	4.3	1.59	31.3	3.8	1.50

been induced to hibernate. One species, *Helix aspersa*, was collected from Crete, where it is exposed to high summer temperatures, but mild winters with very few frosts. *Helix aspersa* is a widespread species and occurs particularly in mild coastal regions. The other species, *H. lucorum*, was collected from a mountainous area in northern Greece, where the summer temperatures are usually mild, but the winters severe. Whereas *H. aspersa* does not always hibernate in the southern part of its range, *H. lucorum* is an obligate hibernator. Hibernation was induced in both species by lowering the temperature from 20 °C to 5 °C, shortening the daylength, and lowering the humidity. The results are given in Tables 2.1 and 2.2.

1. Express the results by drawing two sets of graphs. Describe the effect of temperature on heart rate. Are the results from pre- and post-hibernation likely to be significantly different?

2. (a) What is the effect of acclimation to low temperature on hibernating snails?
   (b) Can you suggest why hibernating snails do not respond in the same way as limpets?

3. (a) What are the temperature coefficients of the four sets of data (between 10 and 20 °C)?
   (b) Discuss possible ecological advantages for the differences in thermal sensitivity of the two species.

Problem 2.2

Distribution of C_3 and C_4 grasses

Background   There are two main forms of photosynthesis in higher plants. In C_3 photosynthesis, CO_2 diffuses passively to the reaction sites in the chloroplasts through the stomata and the air spaces of the leaf mesophyll. In C_4 plants, in contrast, CO_2 is concentrated by an active transport process to the chloroplasts which are located well away from the air spaces in the leaf. This has two advantages. First, the reactions take place in the absence of O_2 so no photorespiration can occur; this process greatly reduces the efficiency of C_3 photosynthesis, especially at high temperatures when O_2 is more soluble in water. Second, C_4 plants can have a higher resistance to air movements through their stomata, which reduces water loss. However, like all active biochemical processes, the CO_2 transport process uses up energy. As a result leaves with C_3 and C_4 photosynthesis show different responses to temperature. Figure 2.2 shows the relationship between net photosynthesis and leaf temperature in pure canopies of C_3 and C_4 species at high light intensities.

Further reading

Begon *et al.* (1986: Ch. 3), Fitter and Hay (1987: Ch. 2), Salisbury and Ross (1992: Ch. 12).

Data and questions   1. Explain the rather different effect of leaf temperature on C_3 and C_4 photosynthesis in the light of the differences between the two processes.

The relative grass species composition and coverage along an altitudinal gradient has been examined in Hawaii Volcanoes National Park (Fig. 2.3). Temperature records are sparse, but at an elevation of 1400 m there is a monthly mean minimum temperature of *c.* 9 °C and a mean maximum temperature of *c.* 21 °C. Precipitation is maximal at about this altitude (2500 mm year^{-1}) with lower levels occurring at sea level (100–1500 mm year^{-1}) and on the mountain summits (*c.* 600 mm year^{-1}).

2. In the light of Figs. 2.2 and 2.3, discuss the features which may be responsible for determining the altitudinal distribution of grass species in the Hawaiian Islands.

Figure 2.2. The relationship between net photosynthesis of C_3 (——) and C_4 (- - - - -) leaf canopies and leaf temperature.

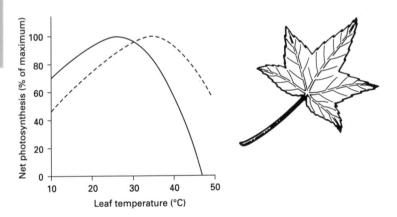

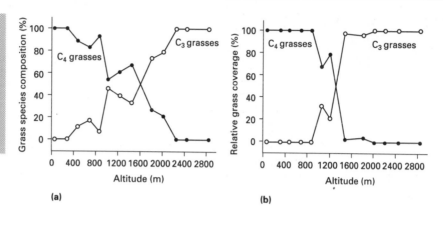

Figure 2.3. The change in a) species composition and b) species coverage of C_3 (○) and C_4 (●) grasses along an altitudinal gradient in Hawaii (from Rundel, 1980).

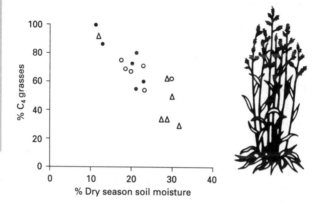

Figure 2.4. The relationship between the dry season moisture content of soil and the incidence of C_4 grasses on Mount Kenya. △ = transects at 3200 m; ○ = transects at 3000 m; ● = transects at 2860 m.

The data depicted in Fig. 2.4 describe the incidence of C_4 grasses as a function of dry season soil moisture within a zone of C_3–C_4 overlap on Mount Kenya. As in Hawaii (Fig. 2.3), C_3 grasses predominate at higher elevations and C_4 grasses at lower altitudes.

3. Explain how the apparently different data in Figs. 2.3 and 2.4 are consistent with each other.

Problem 2.3   Feeding biology of red grouse chicks

Background   The data on which this problem is based are from a study of the ecology of red grouse (*Lagopus lagopus scoticus*) on the northern Pennines and North York Moors. Traditionally grouse moors have been managed by repeated burning so that there is an adequate supply of the young heather shoots on which the adults feed. Grouse chicks, however, have a more varied diet and take, besides heather, a variety of arthropods (see Table 2.3) which give them much of the protein they need for growth. The diet of chicks has been studied by examination of faecal material within which both heather 'bracts' (small leaves with an undeveloped blade) and arthropod skeletal remains may be recognised.

Table 2.3. The arthropod food of red grouse chicks during the first 20 days of life.	Arthropod group	% in diet
	Araneae (spiders, all families)	14
	Coleoptera (Elateridae)	19
	Coleoptera (other families)	6
	Diptera (Tipulidae)	10
	Diptera (other families)	25
	Hemiptera	3
	Hymenoptera (adults)	7
	Caterpillars (Hymenoptera and Lepidoptera)	14
	Other groups	2

Further reading

Warren and Goldsmith (1983: Ch. 7).

Data and questions

Table 2.4 shows the occurrence of heather bracts and of arthropod remains in the droppings of grouse chicks of different ages. The number of bracts are expressed as the estimated intake of bracts per chick per day. Note also that it proved most convenient to check, in sample faecal material, the numbers of arthropods present per 100 bracts rather than to identify and count all the arthropod items separately.

Table 2.5 gives data obtained from ten separate broods of chicks. It compares both chick survival and mean chick weight with the frequency of arthropod items in the faecal material produced by the brood.

1. Investigate and comment on the relationship between chick age and the rate of intake of arthropod food.

2. Investigate and comment on the apparent effect of arthropod food on chick growth and survival.

Table 2.4. Analysis of droppings of grouse chicks of different age.	Age (days)	Number of arthropods per 100 bracts	Estimated daily number of bracts per chick
	2	7.6	220
	4	3.6	460
	6	2.2	680
	8	2.5	710
	10	1.8	880
	12	1.4	930
	14	0.9	1080
	16	0.6	1100
	18	0.3	1160
	20	0.1	1300

Arthropod remains per 100 bracts	Chick survival to 10 days (%)	Average weight of brood at 10 days
2.1	50	35
5.6	60	47
3.4	65	41
2.0	50	40
5.6	80	50
3.5	85	45
0.5	35	30
2.6	50	43
5.1	65	50
2.0	65	42

Table 2.5. Data for chick survival and chick weight gain in ten broods over the first 10 days.

The average density of adult grouse during the nesting season is five per hectare. Average clutch size in grouse is eight and chick mortality during the second 10 days of life continues at the same rate as that during the first 10 days. The estimated density of arthropods on the moor during the grouse breeding season is $100\,\mathrm{m}^{-2}$.

3. Estimate what percentage of arthropods is taken by grouse chicks during the breeding season. Comment on whether feeding by grouse chicks seems likely either to influence the moorland arthropod community or to affect the survival of nearby broods of grouse chicks.

4. Discuss, mentioning any additional experiments that you would wish to carry out, how you could investigate further whether arthropod availability during the breeding season has any influence on recruitment of chicks to the adult grouse population.

Problem 2.4

Defences against leaf damage in birch

Background Plants have two main strategies for chemically defending their leaves from herbivory. First, they can produce small quantities of poisonous compounds, such as alkaloids and cardiac glucosides. This is a very cheap way of deterring most species of animals, but it has the disadvantage that one species may evolve the ability to detoxify the compound which would allow it unlimited access to the plant. The second way is to produce much larger quantities of substances such as tannins and phenolics which make the leaf more difficult and less profitable to digest. This will work against all species but is more expensive. One would therefore expect plants to evolve means of detecting attack and increasing levels of compounds only when they are attacked.

Leaves of birch trees (*Betula* spp.) show changes in several chemical constituents following partial damage, for example of the type caused by caterpillars chewing holes in them. These changes do not occur when entire leaves are removed at the petioles. A series of observations were made to investigate the idea that these chemical changes constitute one form of defence by the plant against attack by caterpillars (the 'defence hypothesis').

Further reading

Begon *et al.* (1986: Chs 3 and 8), Harborne (1988: Ch. 3).

Data and questions

Damage caused by caterpillars can be simulated by punching holes with a paper hole puncher. Table 2.6 shows changes in leaf chemistry that were observed following such artificial damage to half the leaves distributed randomly on otherwise undamaged trees.

Table 2.7 summarises the performance of caterpillars of the moth *Epirrita autumnata* fed on foliage from birch trees. These caterpillars were reared in the laboratory and given fresh leaves collected every day. These leaves were either from control trees with undamaged leaves or damaged leaves from birch trees whose leaves had been experimentally damaged 4–7 days beforehand, using a paper hole puncher.

Table 2.6. Changes in leaf chemistry (total leaf phenolics as % dry weight) prior to damage and after damage simulating insect grazing to five experimental birch trees on 1 June. Three trees acted as undamaged controls. Each measurement of phenolics is the mean of ten leaves per tree on the appropriate date.

	Tree No.	31 May	2 June	4 June
Experimental trees				
Damaged	1	5.5	6.2	6.4
Intact	1	5.6	5.5	5.7
Damaged	2	6.1	6.4	6.6
Intact	2	6.0	6.1	6.6
Damaged	3	6.8	7.2	7.5
Intact	3	7.0	7.3	7.3
Damaged	4	7.1	7.5	7.6
Intact	4	7.1	7.1	7.5
Damaged	5	7.4	7.9	8.0
Intact	5	7.2	7.5	7.7
Control trees (all leaves intact)				
	6	6.8	6.8	6.8
	7	5.4	5.3	5.4
	8	7.3	7.2	7.1

Table 2.7. Performance of *Epirrita* caterpillars reared in the laboratory under controlled conditions on either damaged or undamaged birch leaves. There were about 30 caterpillars in each treatment; data are means ±95% confidence intervals.

Treatment	Duration (egg-pupae) days	Fresh weight of pupae (mg)	
		Male	Female
Fed damaged leaves	35 ±1.5	61 ± 2.5	68 ± 0.7
Fed intact leaves	30 ± 0.99	65 ± 1.4	84 ± 1.1

Weight of female pupa (mg)	Eggs per female
70	3
72	5
74	9
78	24
80	39
82	64

Table 2.8. Effect of pupal weight on total number of eggs laid per female *Epirrita*.

Tree	Height (m)	Phenolics (% dry wt)	Number of caterpillars
A	0.80	5.1	15
B	1.10	6.1	51
C	0.50	5.8	6
D	0.90	7.4	39
E	0.95	6.0	26
F	1.20	7.1	31
G	1.03	5.6	30
H	0.60	6.4	19
I	1.24	5.3	62
J	0.72	6.7	22

Table 2.9. Total numbers of *Epirrita* caterpillars on birch trees in the field. Caterpillars were counted when about three-quarters grown using a reliable method. Phenolic contents are the means of ten leaves per tree.

Epirrita has a single well synchronised generation each year. Caterpillars hatch in the spring from eggs laid on twigs the previous autumn. Following pupation the adults fly and disperse widely. The fecundity of the females is related to their size as indicated in Table 2.8.

Table 2.9 records the actual number of *Epirrita* caterpillars found in the field on each of a series of birch trees, and also gives information about the size and chemistry of each tree.

1. Use Table 2.6 to determine the effect of damaging leaves on total leaf phenolic level: plot the data and comment on the results.

2. Calculate the effect of feeding damaged leaves to caterpillars on the fecundity of adult female moths. Show how you obtained your results.

3 (a) Is there any relationship between leaf phenolic levels and caterpillar numbers?
(b) What appears to be the most important determinant of the number of caterpillars per tree?
(c) Do your analyses suggest that phenolics in birch leaves act as a defence?

4. Comment on the design of these experiments, paying particular attention to any inconsistencies in methodology. Can experiments such as these be used either to support or refute the 'defence hypothesis'?

27

Problem 2.5 Olfactory attraction in hyperparasites

Background

Parasitism is common in the Hymenoptera. Many 'parasitoid' wasps lay their eggs on or in other species of insect, their larvae eating the host alive, before finally killing it, pupating and emerging. Some of the 'hyperparasitoids' even parasitise other parasitoids. In both cases the ability to find the host is a crucial part of their biology.

The aphid *Myzus persicae* feeds on several species of plants. One of its important natural enemies is the parasitoid *Diaeretiella rapae* (Hymenoptera) which in turn is attacked by the hyperparasitoid *Charips brassicae* (Hymenoptera). *Charips* only attacks aphids already parasitised by *Diaeretiella*. Parasitised aphids become mummified; by breeding out mummies, therefore, it is easy to discover whether they give rise to parasitoids (*Diaeretiella*) or to hyperparasitoids (*Charips*). Hyperparasitised aphids only give rise to *Charips* because *Charips* kills *Diaeretiella*.

Further reading

Begon *et al.* (1986: Ch. 9).

Data and questions

Table 2.10 records the percentage of aphids from which *Diaeretiella* and *Charips* were reared in collections from two adjacent fields: one of potatoes, the other of cabbages. The crops were sampled on the same day using similar methods. *Myzus* densities in different parts of the two fields have been expressed per 100 cm^2 of crop-leaf surface to aid comparison.

Laboratory studies on responses of *Diaeretiella* and *Charips* to various odours are reported in Table 2.11. These data were obtained in an olfactometer: an apparatus that allows the insect to choose without bias between an experimental odour and a control with no odour. Insects are run singly and their responses recorded. Insects in the olfactometer cannot see the experimental chamber or control chamber or what they contain; they can respond only to odours emanating from the chambers.

1. Analyse and comment on the percentage of *Myzus* attacked by *Diaeretiella* in the two crops.

Table 2.10. Mean population densities of *Myzus persicae* on the same date in different areas of two crops in adjacent fields, together with estimates of the percentages of these aphids parasitised by *Diaeretiella* or hyperparasitised by *Charips*. Each estimate of aphid density and associated data is based on a sample of aphids and plants taken from a small area; with each sample, leaf areas were estimated, the aphids counted, and then reared to obtain parasitoids or hyperparasitoids.

Cabbages			Potatoes		
	% with			% with	
Aphids per 100 cm^2	Diaeretiella	Charips	Aphids per 100 cm^2	Diaeretiella	Charips
10	13.9	5.6	13	0.0	0.1
17	9.0	19.2	24	1.2	0.0
30	36.0	6.0	48	0.7	0.1
72	36.1	14.9	121	0.0	0.0
145	15.5	34.0	300	1.3	0.0
790	33.6	20.4			

Table 2.11. Responses of *Diaeretiella* and *Charips* to various odours in laboratory olfactometer experiments.	Material providing experimental odour	Test animal	Number of test animals choosing chamber		
			Neither	Experimental	Control
	Cabbage leaves	*Diaeretiella* ♀	2	84	6
		Diaeretiella ♂	25	21	19
		Charips ♀	27	3	4
		Charips ♂	14	2	1
	Potato leaves	*Diaeretiella* ♀	27	5	7
		Charips ♀	9	1	0
	Live *Myzus* on moist filter paper	*Diaeretiella* ♀	1	29	1
		Diaeretiella ♂	14	2	3
		Charips ♀	10	0	0
		Charips ♂	17	0	1
	Live female *Diaeretiella*	*Diaeretiella* ♀	25	28	31
		Diaeretiella ♂	7	26	8
		Charips ♀	0	16	2
		Charips ♂	13	0	0

2. Interpret these data to explain how female *Diaeretiella* may locate suitable populations of hosts in the field and hence how the results in Table 2.10 might be generated.

3. How do female *Charips* apparently find suitable populations of hosts?

4. How do male *Diaeretiella* and male *Charips* find mates? For one of these species an additional experiment would be helpful; briefly say what it is.

5. Although you are not expected to carry out statistical tests on these data, how would you analyse them more rigorously if called on to do so?

6. Briefly outline two further observations or experiments that you might carry out on this plant – parasitoid – hyperparasitoid food chain to elucidate problems with the existing data and their interpretation, or to learn more about the system.

Problem 2.6   Foraging strategies of moose

Background   Our understanding of the feeding behaviour of animals has been much increased in recent years by behavioural ecologists, who have developed the theory of 'optimal foraging'. This suggests that animals behave, subject to certain constraints, in a way that maximises some aspect of food intake, such as the rate of energy gain. By combining this theory with detailed field studies on particular species, they have been remarkably successful in explaining many aspects of feeding behaviour. The following question deals with just such a study.

Further reading

Krebs and Davies (1993: Ch. 3), Begon *et al.* (1986: Ch. 9), Belovsky (1978).

Data and questions

Moose (*Alces alces*) living in the Isle Royale National Park on Lake Superior, Michigan, have a choice of two habitats in which to feed: forest, where they browse on deciduous leaves, and small lakes, where they crop aquatic vegetation. A field study (Belovsky 1978) found that the diet of a 360 kg bull moose is constrained by three factors:

1. It must obtain at least 1.9 g of sodium each day.

2. It requires at least 5.0×10^7 J of energy each day.

3. The maximum weight of food the moose can eat is restricted to 32 kg each day by the size and digestive capacity of its rumen.

Examination of the vegetation showed that both aquatic and terrestrial plants have an extractable energy content of 17 kJ g^{-1} of dry matter, but that terrestrial vegetation has a much higher dry matter content, 25 per cent, compared with only 5 per cent for aquatic vegetation. However aquatic vegetation is rich in sodium which constitutes 0.3 per cent of its dry weight, while terrestrial plants contain a negligible amount.

1. Calculate the minimum weight of aquatic vegetation the moose must eat daily to satisfy its sodium requirements. Can it process this amount?

2. Calculate the minimum weight of terrestrial vegetation the moose must eat daily to satisfy its daily energy requirements. Can it process this amount?

3. Calculate the minimum weight of aquatic vegetation the moose must eat daily to satisfy its daily energy requirements. Can it process this amount?

4. Draw a graph of the daily intake of aquatic vegetation against the daily intake of terrestrial vegetation which shows how the diet of the moose is constrained by the three factors of sodium requirement, energy requirement and rumen capacity. Can a moose survive by eating one type of vegetation alone?

5. What diet will maximise the energy intake of the moose subject to the other constraints on its diet and what will its daily net energy gain be if it eats in this way?

6. A female moose requires a further 1.2 g of sodium per day to nourish its calf. What effect will this have on the diet it must choose and on its maximum daily net energy gain?

SOLUTIONS

Problem 2.1

1. See Figs 2.5 and 2.6. Heart rates increase exponentially with temperature in all four data sets, between the temperatures 6 and 24 °C. In *Helix aspersa* heart rates at lower temperatures are lower when the animals are in hibernation than when acclimated to the higher temperature, and these differences appear to be significantly different (the standard error bars do not overlap), but at higher

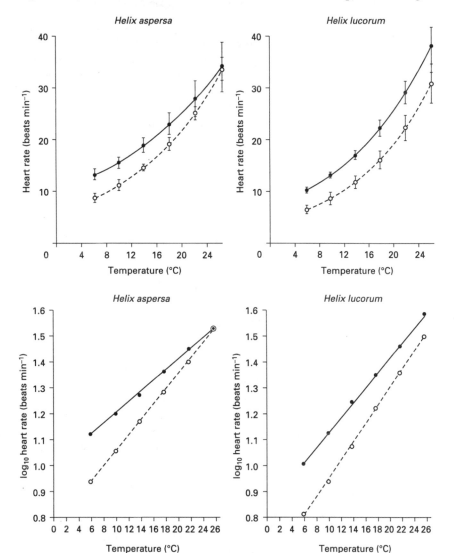

Figure 2.5. Mean heart rates of eight *Helix aspersa* (left) and six *Helix lucorum* (right) in late autumn, immediately before (●) and 13 days after (○) inducing hibernation by transferring from 20 °C to 5 °C.

Figure 2.6. Log$_{10}$ of the mean heart rates of eight *Helix aspersa* (left) and six *Helix lucorum* (right) in late autumn, immediately before (●) and 13 days after (○) inducing hibernation by transferring from 20 °C to 5 °C.

temperatures, the acclimation conditions appear to have no effect. In *H. lucorum* the heart rates are lower when the animals are in hibernation conditions than when at elevated temperatures, at all test temperatures. These differences are likely to be significant, at least over the lower range of test temperatures, but the rates are more variable at elevated temperatures, and more data are required in this region.

2. (a) In both species, animals acclimated to lower temperatures of hibernation have, at any selected test temperature, lower heart rates than when kept at elevated non-hibernating temperatures, i.e. the snails show reverse acclimation. In *H. aspersa*, this acclimation is accomplished by rotation of the graph about a temperature of approximately 26 °C, so that the animals show increased temperature sensitivity in hibernation; in *H. lucorum* it is accomplished by translation of the graph downwards.

(b) The acclimation responses of the hibernating land snails are the reverse of those shown by the marine limpet *Acmaea*. In the winter, the limpet needs to adjust its metabolic rate to compensate for the lowered environmental temperatures, whereas the hibernating land snails need to conserve energy by reducing their metabolism.

3. (a) The temperature coefficients are obtained by interpolating the rate at 20 °C from the log rate graphs. The rates at 10 and 20 °C, and the Q_{10} values, are therefore:

	10 °C	20 °C	Q_{10}
H. aspersa at 20 °C	15.9	antilog of 1.41 = 25.7	25.7/15.9 = 1.62
H. aspersa at 5 °C	11.4	antilog of 1.33 = 21.4	21.4/11.4 = 1.88
H. lucorum at 20 °C	13.2	antilog of 1.41 = 25.7	25.7/13.2 = 1.95
H. lucorum at 5 °C	8.8	antilog of 1.29 = 19.5	19.5/ 8.8 = 2.25

(b) *H. lucorum* shows higher thermal sensitivity than *H. aspersa* in both hibernating and non-hibernating conditions (it has a higher Q_{10}). In winter this allows this obligate hibernator to conserve energy by reducing metabolism more. In summer, it may make the snail more responsive to changes in temperature, governing the entry into hibernation. It also shows greater acclimation to winter conditions; in hibernating conditions its heart rate is greatly reduced at all temperatures. This has two advantages: it will save energy and reduce the activity in the winter even if there is a period of mild weather. This will stop it coming out and being hit by a subsequent frost. The Cretan *H. aspersa* shows much less acclimation for hibernation, particularly at high temperatures. This will allow it to take advantage of mild periods in the winter, while because of the mild Cretan winters it is unlikely to be injured by frost.

Problem 2.2 1. The C_4 canopy has a higher optimum temperature for photosynthesis than the C_3 canopy. This is because at high temperatures there is a high rate of photorespiration in C_3 plants which limits net photosynthesis. In contrast, at low temperatures the high cost of transporting CO_2 in C_4 plants outweighs any benefits conferred by preventing the small amount of photorespiration.

2. Figure 2.3 shows that C_3 grasses tend to be confined to land above 1400 m and C_4 grasses to land below 1400 m. These differences are probably due to temperature differences up the mountain. At higher altitudes temperatures are lower and C_3 grasses, with their better low-temperature performance, would be expected to grow faster. At lower altitudes where temperatures are higher, in contrast, C_4 plants should perform better. At first sight it might seem that there is an inconsistency between the data from the two graphs. At the height at which species composition changes the mean air temperature is about 15 °C, whereas the temperature at which C_4 plants start to outperform C_3 plants is about 30 °C. However, the absorption of sunlight warms leaves to well above the temperature of the surrounding air, so at 1400 m the mean daytime leaf temperature *is* probably around 30 °C.

3. The data in Fig. 2.4 show that on Mount Kenya the altitude at which species composition of grasses changes from C_3 to C_4 species occurs much higher than in Hawaii, at about 3000 m. The anomaly is probably due to differences in the availability of water at the two sites and to the different water-use efficiencies of C_3 and C_4 plants. Because of their CO_2 concentrating mechanism, C_4 plants can maintain the optimum intercellular concentration of CO_2 at the chloroplasts at higher stomatal resistances than C_3 plants. Therefore they lose less water and should survive longer on droughted soil. On Mount Kenya soils below 3000 m tend to become very dry in the dry season, so C_4 plants would be favoured even though the temperature of their leaves is probably below the optimum. In Hawaii there seems to be no clear gradient of moisture with height as the rainfall peaks at 1400 m, so the differences in the grasses with respect to temperature alone influence their distribution.

Problem 2.3

1. (The number of arthropods eaten each day is given by multiplying number of arthropods per 100 bracts by the number of bracts, and dividing by 100.) For the first 10 days of their life the chicks consume arthropods at a constant rate, around

Figure 2.7. The relationship between the age of grouse chicks and the number of arthropods they eat.

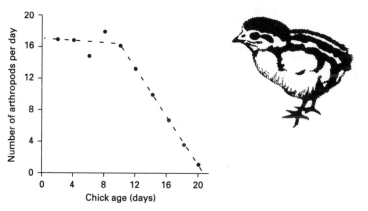

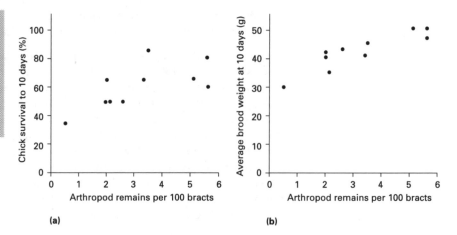

Figure 2.8. The relationship between the amount of arthropod food eaten by chicks and (a) chick survival; (b) the average weight of the brood, both at 10 days.

sixteen per day (see Fig. 2.7) but after 10 days consumption falls approximately linearly until by 20 days they are hardly eating any arthropods. This is in contrast with the consumption of bracts which carries on increasing as the chicks get older so their diet becomes more and more like the herbivorous diet of adults.

2. There seems to be a fairly good correlation between the amount of arthropod food chicks eat and their growth in weight (Fig. 2.8(b)), and a similar, but weaker, correlation between the amount of arthropod food eaten and survival (Fig. 2.8(a)). In general, grouse which eat more arthropods put on weight faster and also tend to be more likely to survive. However, this correlation does not necessarily imply a causal relationship. Grouse *may* grow faster and survive better because they eat more arthropods. On the other hand, it might be the case that larger, healthier chicks are better at catching arthropods. Yet another explanation might be that chick survival is related to the quality of the territory their parents have established; more survive on territories which produce more heather bracts and which, as a by-product, harbour more invertebrates. Beware of inferring a causal relationship from a correlation.

3. Since there are on average five grouse per hectare, half of which will be female, there will be 2.5 nests per hectare. Since there are eight chicks per clutch their initial density will be

$$2.5 \times 8 = 20 \text{ ha}^{-1}$$

The average survival to 10 days is around 60 per cent, so the average density of live chicks during the first 10 days is about 80 per cent of the total:

$$20 \times 0.8 = 16 \text{ ha}^{-1}$$

Since each chick eats about sixteen arthropods a day in its first 10 days an average chick will eat 160 arthropods. The total number eaten will be

$$16 \times 160 = 2560 \text{ ha}^{-1}$$

34

During the second 10 days there will be fewer chicks and on average each will eat fewer arthropods. Since mortality continues at the same rate there will be

$$0.6 \times 0.6 \times 20 = 7.2 \text{ chicks ha}^{-1}$$

after 20 days, but on average from 10 to 20 days there will be

$$0.6 \times 0.8 \times 20 = 9.6 \text{ chicks ha}^{-1}.$$

Each will eat on average only half the amount consumed in the first 10 days = 80 arthropods. The total number eaten in the second 10 days is therefore

$$9.6 \times 80 = 768 \text{ ha}^{-1}$$

The total number of arthropods eaten by the chicks is therefore

$$2560 + 768 = 3328 \text{ ha}^{-1}$$
$$= 0.33 \text{ m}^{-2}$$

Only just over 0.3 per cent of the arthropods will be eaten by the grouse so grouse predation will have little influence on the arthropod community or on the survival of nearby broods.

4. The data which have been given give no information about how arthropod availability affects recruitment of the chicks to the adult population. One study that could be performed would be to monitor arthropod numbers in different areas on the moor and measure the survival of chicks in those areas. However, there may be other differences between sites, such as bract availability, which also influence survival.

   A better test would be to alter arthropod densities experimentally at different sites. Insects on several sites could be hoovered up just before the chicks hatch to produce a low arthropod density and these could be placed on other sites to produce high arthropod density. In control plots arthropods would be left in place. The amount of disturbance should as far as possible be made equal at all the sites. Survival of chicks at the different sites could then be monitored.

Problem 2.4

1. Total leaf phenolic level rises after leaf damage. The level rises fastest and by the greatest amount in the damaged leaves themselves (Fig. 2.9): most of the increase occurs in the first 2 days after damage, and after 4 days the phenolic level has risen by an average of around 0.6 per cent. In the undamaged leaves the increase in phenolic level is only around 0.4 per cent and is delayed, being greatest between days 2 and 4. The increase in the level of phenolics seems to be small but significant in both cases.

2. Feeding female caterpillars on damaged leaves will reduce their pupal weight from 84 to 68 mg. The effect this has on adult fecundity can best be calculated using a graph drawn from the data in Table 2.8 (Fig. 2.10). The numbers of eggs laid by

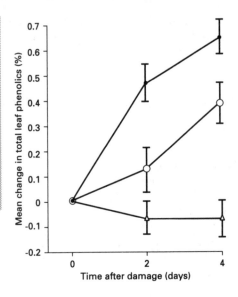

Figure 2.9. The effect of damaging leaves on leaf phenolic levels. The graph shows the mean change in total leaf phenolics of damaged (●) and intact leaves (○), 2 and 4 days after wounding. △ shows results from control trees. Error bars show the standard error of the mean.

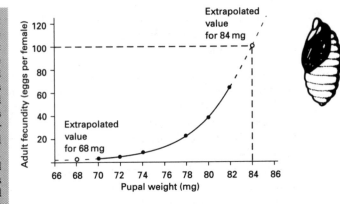

Figure 2.10. The effect of pupal weight on the fecundity of adult females. Data values are given as ● and interpolated values estimated by the solid line. The curve is extrapolated to higher and lower pupal weights (broken line). The estimated fecundity of adults which have been fed undamaged (84 mg) and damaged (68 mg) leaves is then found from this extrapolation (○).

adults from pupae weighing 68 and 84 mg have to be extrapolated from the graph because no data are available for these extreme weights. We calculated that 84 mg females should lay 100 eggs and 68 mg females should lay only 2. Feeding on damaged leaves should therefore reduce fecundity by around 98 per cent.

3. (a) A graph plotting the number of caterpillars in a tree against the level of phenolics it contains (Fig. 2.11) shows that there is no relationship between the two numbers.

   (b) The most important determinant for the number of caterpillars in a tree appears to be its height (Fig. 2.12): taller trees have more caterpillars, probably because they have more leaves.

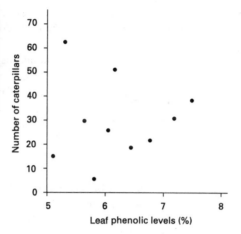

Figure 2.11. The relationship between the leaf phenolic levels of a tree and the number of caterpillars on it.

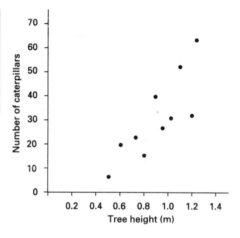

Figure 2.12. The relationship between the height of a tree and the numbers of caterpillars found on it.

(c) These results suggest that phenolics in birch *might* act as a defence against caterpillars, since feeding insects on damaged leaves slows their development and reduces their ultimate weight. The size of the next generation would therefore be reduced. However, one cannot tell whether the phenolics actually deterred the caterpillars from eating the leaves.

4. The design of the experiments was generally poor. First, no data were available for the fecundity of light and heavy females and therefore data had to be extrapolated (Fig. 2.10) which is always a risky procedure. Second, the experiments could be used neither to support, nor to refute, the 'defence hypothesis'. To do this it is necessary to test whether increased levels of phenolics in leaves actually reduce the damage caused by caterpillars. The experiments which were carried out showed that eating damaged leaves reduced the growth of the caterpillars. However, they did not demonstrate that this was because they contained higher levels of

phenolics; it might have been because damaged leaves had lower food value. Neither did they show that caterpillars ate different amounts of the two sorts of leaves.

To test the hypothesis further, experiments should be carried out both in the field and laboratory. First, the extent of caterpillar damage should be monitored in different trees in the field, and related to the levels of phenolics in their leaves. Second, caterpillars could be supplied with leaves containing different levels of phenolics to test which they would choose.

Problem 2.5

1. The percentage of *Myzus* attacked by *Diaeretiella* is the sum of the percentage containing *Diaeretiella* and those containing *Charips*. This is because *Charips* only attacks *Myzus* which have already been infected by *Diaeretiella*.

   Fig. 2.13 shows a graph of the percentage of *Myzus* attacked against their population density. There is a big difference between the two crops. There is heavy parasitism in the cabbage field and the incidence rises with the population density of *Myzus*. In the potato field the incidence of parasitism is much lower and there is no relationship with population density.

2. *Diaeretiella* locates host populations by smell. Initially they are attracted to cabbages, a plant on which aphids commonly feed and once in a cabbage field and close to their hosts they are led to them by the smell of the aphids themselves. This explains firstly why parasitism is so low in the field of potatoes, to which *Diaeretiella* is not attracted. Second, it explains why the incidence of parasitism rises with the host density; a higher density of aphids will produce a more powerful smell and attract parasites more strongly.

3. Female *Charips* also find populations of hosts by smell; they are attracted to the scent of female *Diaeretiella* which will probably be found near the aphids they have parasitised. They are not attracted to cabbage or aphids.

Figure 2.13. The relationship between the population density of *Myzus persicae* and the percentage which are attacked by parasitoids for aphids in fields of cabbage (●) and potatoes (○). Log values of density are used.

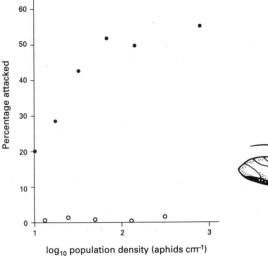

Percentage attacked

$\log_{10}$ population density (aphids cm^{-1})

4. Male *Diaeretiella* also seem to find mates by using their sense of smell; they are attracted to the scent of female *Diaeretiella*. The data do not tell us how male *Charips* find mates. It is possible that they too may find the female by smell, but a further olfactometer experiment must be carried out to test this idea. Males must be run through an olfactometer which has female *Charips* in the experimental chamber.

5. The olfactometer data are best analysed by carrying out a chi-squared test on each set of data. This should test the null hypothesis that equal numbers of insects choose the experimental and control chambers (insects which make no response can be ignored). If the chi-squared test shows a significant departure in behaviour from the null hypothesis, this shows that insects are probably attracted to or repelled by the experimental scent.

   Consider the response of female *Diaeretiella* to cabbage leaves. Out of 90 which respond to the scent, 84 go towards it and 6 away. The expected numbers, if the scent had no effect, would be 45 to each. A contingency table can be drawn up.

	Odour	Control
Expected	45	45
Observed	84	6

$$\text{Chi-squared} = \sum \left[\frac{(\text{Observed} - \text{expected})^2}{\text{Expected}} \right]$$

$$= \left[\frac{(84 - 45)^2}{45} + \frac{(6 - 45)^2}{45} \right]$$

$$= 33.8 + 33.8$$

$$= 67.6$$

The 95 per cent significance level of chi-squared for one degree of freedom is only 3.84 so in this case there is clearly a significant bias towards the experimental odour.

An alternative would be to test the distribution against the expected binomial distribution.

6. One experiment would be to test the reactions of female *Charips* to parasitised and unparasitised aphids, to investigate how they locate the correct hosts. A simple olfactometer experiment with parasitised aphids as the experimental odour should be performed.

   Female *Diaeretiella* might also be expected to avoid female *Charips*. Female *Diaeretiella* should be run through an olfactometer in which female *Charips* is the experimental odour to test whether this response occurs and is mediated by smell.

   The aphids might also be expected to avoid female *Diaeretiella* so they too could be run through an olfactometer with female *Diaeretiella* as the experimental odour.

However, since aphids are usually sedentary creatures and rarely seem to flee from danger this experiment is less likely to be crowned with success.

Problem 2.6 1. The moose must obtain 1.9 g sodium from aquatic vegetation which contains 5 per cent dry matter of which 0.3 per cent is sodium. Therefore

$$\text{Amount required} \times 0.05 \times 0.003 = 1.9 \text{ g}$$

Rearranging the equation

$$\text{Amount required} = 1.9/(0.05 \times 0.003) \text{ g}$$
$$= 12.7 \times 10^3 \text{ g}$$
$$= 13 \text{ kg to two significant figures (can be processed)}.$$

2. The moose must obtain 5×10^7 J from terrestrial vegetation which yields 17 kJ g^{-1} of dry matter and has a dry matter content of 25 per cent. Therefore

$$\text{Amount required} \times 17\,000 \times 0.25 = 5 \times 10^7 \text{ J}$$

Rearranging the equation

$$\text{Amount required} = 5 \times 10^7/(17\,000 \times 0.25) \text{ g}$$
$$= 11.8 \times 10^3 \text{ g}$$
$$= 12 \text{ kg to two significant figures (can be processed)}.$$

3. The moose must obtain 5×10^7 J from aquatic vegetation which yields 17 kJ g^{-1} of dry matter and has a dry matter content of 5 per cent. Therefore

$$\text{Amount required} \times 17\,000 \times 0.05 = 5 \times 10^7 \text{ J}$$

Rearranging the equation

$$\text{Amount required} = 5 \times 10^7/(17\,000 \times 0.05) \text{ g}$$
$$= 58.8 \times 10^3 \text{ g}$$
$$= 59 \text{ kg to two significant figures}$$

The moose would not be able to eat this much food.

4. The only possible range of diets is given by the shaded triangle in Fig. 2.14. The moose must eat a mixture of the two foods to acquire enough energy and sodium. It could not survive on aquatic vegetation alone because it could not extract enough energy from it, while it could not survive on terrestrial vegetation alone because it would get no sodium.

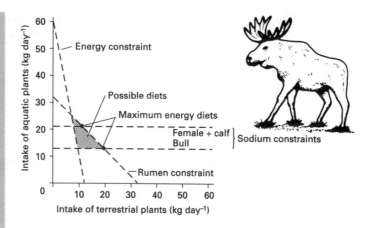

Figure 2.14. Graph showing how the diet of moose is constrained by both the requirements for energy and sodium and by rumen capacity. The shaded area shows the range of possible diets and the closed circles (●) show the diets which maximise energy intake for bulls and for females with calves.

5. Energy intake will be maximised by a diet which is at the bottom right-hand corner of the triangle of feasible diets in Fig. 2.14. At this point the moose is eating the maximum amount of high-energy terrestrial vegetation and the minimum amount of aquatic vegetation to supply its sodium needs, i.e. it is eating 19 kg of terrestrial vegetation and 13 kg of aquatic vegetation (taking values from the graph). Its daily energy intake will be

$$(19 \times 10^3 \times 0.25 \times 17 \times 10^3) + (13 \times 10^3 \times 0.05 \times 17 \times 10^3)$$
$$= (8.08 \times 10^7) + (1.12 \times 10^7) \, J$$
$$= 9.2 \times 10^7 \, J$$

Since its energy requirement is 5.0×10^7 J its net energy gain will be

$$(9.2 \times 10^7) - (5.0 \times 10^7) = 4.2 \times 10^7 \, J$$

6. With a calf to support the female moose must have an intake of $1.9 + 1.2 = 3.1$ g of sodium. It must therefore eat more aquatic vegetation.

Amount required $\times 0.05 \times 0.003 = 3.1$ g

Rearranging the equation

Amount required $= 3.1/(0.05 \times 0.003)$ g
$$= 20.7 \times 10^3 \, g$$
$$= 21 \text{ kg to two significant figures}$$

If this constraint is put into Fig. 2.14 it can be seen that this reduces the possible range of diets to a much smaller triangle. The maximum energy intake will be reduced since the female will be able to eat less energy-rich terrestrial vegetation.

The maximum energy input is again at the bottom right hand of the triangle at which the female eats 11 kg of terrestrial vegetation and 21 kg of aquatic vegetation. Its daily energy intake will be:

$$(11 \times 10^3 \times 0.25 \times 17 \times 10^3) + (21 \times 10^3 \times 0.05 \times 17 \times 10^3)$$

$$= 4.68 \times 10^7 + 1.79 \times 10^7 \text{ J}$$

$$= 6.5 \times 10^7 \text{ J}$$

Since its energy requirements are 5.0×10^7 J its net energy gain will be 6.5×10^7 $- 5.0 \times 10^7 = 1.5 \times 10^7$ J, much lower than the bull.

3

ENERGY AND MINERAL CYCLES

Human daily carbon output in respiration

Background   The burning of fossil fuels (80 per cent) and the destruction of large areas of forest (20 per cent) have both resulted in the release of large amounts of sequestered carbon over the last century in the form of carbon dioxide. It is thought that the increased concentration of carbon dioxide which has resulted may accentuate the 'greenhouse effect' produced by the water vapour and carbon dioxide already present in our atmosphere. This will cause the temperature of the earth to rise, particularly near the poles. However, since there is now also a large human population, each of whom exhales carbon dioxide in each breath, it is possible that we might have a more direct effect on carbon dioxide levels.

Further reading

Readings from *Scientific American* (1973: Ch. 24).

Data and questions

1. Estimate the amount of carbon dioxide your body produces in a day. (This question involves 'ball parking' so you are given no data. You will have to think a bit about your own physiology, anatomy and appetite and combine your knowledge with some of the information given in Table 1.1 to work it out.)

2. Given that the world population is around 5 billion and the world consumption of fossil fuels is around 150 million barrels of oil equivalent per day (1 barrel contains 40 US gallons of oil, a weight of about 150 kg) do you think human respiration will play a significant part in global warming?

Problem 3.2

Carbon dioxide emissions by a factory and carbon fixation by a forest

Background   One possible solution to the problem of the greenhouse effect is to plant large areas of land with trees. The woods will absorb carbon dioxide as they grow, sequestering it in the form of wood and so reducing the concentration in the atmosphere. A recent study carried out in Manchester sought to find out how practical this approach could be.

Tree age (years)	C fixation (kg C m^{-2} year^{-1})
5	0.02
10	0.7
15	1.4
20	2.1

Table 3.1. The relationship between the age of a tree and its rate of carbon fixation.

Further reading

Readings from *Scientific American* (1973: Chs 24 and 25).

Data and questions

One hundred people are employed in a light engineering firm in Lancashire. The annual emission of carbon dioxide, measured as tonnes of carbon per year, before improvements was 246. In 1994 this was reduced to 190 t yr^{-1} carbon, and held at that level, by an energy management scheme, and by switching from petrol to diesel. The management intends to plant sufficient 1-year-old pine trees in 1994 that, after 20 years, the trees will have fixed (in their trunks, roots, etc.) an amount of carbon equivalent to that produced by the factory in the 20 years since 1994. At optimal planting density, the amount of carbon fixed per square metre per year by pine trees of different ages is given in Table 3.1. Note that in the first 5 years carbon fixation is so low it can be assumed to be zero, but thereafter the amount of carbon fixed each year increases at a rate which can be assumed to be linear.

1. Calculate the number of hectares which must be planted with 1 year old pine trees in order to achieve zero net emission from factory plus forest over a period of 20 years.

2. Given that the population of the UK is 55 million, and the total land area is 15 million ha, and assuming that (1) non-employed people (children, houseworkers, etc.) account for two-thirds of the population, (2) employed persons create carbon emissions equal to the workers in the above factory, and (3) a non-employed person creates carbon emissions one-quarter that of a worker, then calculate what percentage of the total land area must be planted with pine forest to give zero net emission over the initial 20-year period from planting.

Problem 3.3

Energy budgets of limpets

Background

Sound scientific knowledge about the movement of energy through ecosystems is essential if resources are to be managed rationally. From 1964 to 1974 there was a concerted world-wide attempt under the aegis of the International Biological Programme (IBP) to gather information on the productivity of ecological communities and to determine the factors which influence it. Of course, before ecosystems can be understood it is essential to understand the energy budgets of individual organisms.

The standard IBP energy budget equation describes the net energy exchange in an individual organism. Carefully constructed, such budgets can help to produce an understanding of energy transfer in ecosystems.

$$C = P_g + P_r + R + F + U$$

where C is consumption, P_g is somatic growth, P_r is reproductive investment, R is respiration, F is faeces and U is excretion.

Assimilation (A) is

$$A = P_g + P_r + R + U$$

Further reading

Begon *et al.* (1986: Ch. 17), Phillipson (1966).

Data and questions

Wright and Hartnoll in 1981 assumed mucus production by the limpet *Patella vulgata* on a shore on the Isle of Man was 8 per cent of the energy assimilated from food, and included it in the U term of a population energy budget, which in kJ m^{-2} year^{-1} was

$$1605 = 68 + 96 + 498 + 884 + 59$$
$$ C_s \quad P_g \quad P_r \quad R \quad F \quad U$$

where C_s is the sum of the other measured terms. But their *measured* value of consumption, C_m, was 2227 kJ m^{-2} year^{-1}, and this was rejected as an overestimate.

Davies in 1991 measured mucus production of individual limpets from the same shore, in June, and found that in air (and, therefore, not moving) the amount of mucus, y, was

$$y = 7.237 \times 10^{-6} \times x^{1.19} \text{ g dry weight hour}^{-1},$$

and in water (and moving) it was

$$y = 8.51 \times 10^{-6} \times x^{1.90} \text{ g dry weight hour}^{-1},$$

where x = shell length in millimetres. On the shore the mean shell length was 38 mm. The population density was 12.6 m^{-2}.

1. Calculate the daily mucus production per square metre of shore (a) in air, and (b) in water.

2. Assuming limpets are in air 12 hours each day and in water 12 hours each day, calculate the yearly mucus production from limpets per metre of shore.

3. If the calorific value of mucus (determined by micro–bomb calorimetry) is 8.98 kJ g^{-1} dry weight, calculate yearly expenditure of energy in mucus.

4. Recalculate C_s using Wright and Hartnoll's data, but adding the mucus term calculated by Davies (and remembering to remove Wright and Hartnoll's estimate of mucus production).

5. Express mucus production as a proportion of energy assimilated.

Problem 3.4	Nitrogen cycling in an evergreen forest

Background

Nitrogen is needed by all organisms, as it is an important component of proteins. Despite its abundance in the atmosphere, however, nitrogen is often a limiting resource to growth because of its inertness; atmospheric nitrogen is converted to the usable forms of ammonium (and subsequently nitrate) only by the slow process of nitrogen fixation, which can be carried out only by certain bacteria. Many ecosystems therefore have a very low net input of nitrogen. In these systems it is essential to cycle the nitrogen which is present if productivity is to be maintained, so death and decomposition, which release nitrogen, are important parts of most ecosystems.

Further reading

Sprent (1987), Readings from *Scientific American* (1973: Ch. 26).

Data and questions

This question refers to a mature Douglas fir ecosystem in Oregon, USA, in which there was no net growth. Table 3.2 gives data on the biomass of the main components of the ecosystem and the mean nitrogen content of each component. It also gives data on the 'throughput' between components: the fall of litter to the forest floor (mostly in the autumn) and its subsequent decay; the growth of mycorrhizas (to a maximum in early summer) and their subsequent decay; and the growth of fungi to a maximum in winter and their subsequent decay. All of these figures were obtained by lengthy

Table 3.2. Maximum biomass, throughput and nitrogen content of the components of a mature Douglas fir ecosystem.

	Biomass (kg ha^{-1})	Throughput (kg ha^{-1})	Nitrogen content (%)
Aerial parts	260 000	3 200	0.16
Roots	49 000	0	0.08
Mycorrhizas	25 000	14 600	0.62
Forest floor	19 000	3 000	0.47
Fungi	23 000	9 200	0.80
Soil organic matter	450 000	n.d.	1.70

n.d. = not determined.

surveys of the biomass of each component thoughout the year. There was negligible nitrogen fixation or leaching of nitrogen, so this was essentially a closed system.

1. (a) Calculate the maximum amount of nitrogen retained in each component of the ecosystem. Where is most of the nitrogen to be found?

   (b) Estimate the amount of nitrogen throughput between each component. What assumptions did you have to make? Are they justified?

2. Use your results to produce as far as possible a complete nitrogen cycle for the forest. Which is the most important component in this nitrogen cycle?

SOLUTIONS

Problem 3.1

1. There are many possible ways to answer this question. One is to estimate the volume of carbon dioxide you produce by using your knowledge of lung physiology. Air entering the lungs usually has a negligible amount of carbon dioxide, but at the surface of the alveoli oxygen in the air is exchanged for carbon dioxide in the blood; air leaving the lungs contains around 4 per cent carbon dioxide. Though the *total* volume of the lungs is around 4 l, when you are at rest the tidal volume of each breath is more like 1 l. At each breath you therefore expel $1 \times 0.04 = 0.04$ l of carbon dioxide. The total volume produced in a day will depend on how fast you breathe. A person at rest breathes about fifteen times per minute (one breath every 4 seconds) and there are 60 minutes in an hour and 24 hours a day. The total number of breaths per day is therefore $15 \times 60 \times 24 = 21\,600$. The total volume produced is therefore $0.04 \times 21\,600 = 864$ l.

How much will this weigh? Well, from chemistry you should have learnt that 1 mol of any gas takes up a volume of 24 l at room temperature and pressure. Therefore you will have produced $864/24 = 36$ mol of carbon dioxide. The molecular weights of carbon and oxygen are 12 and 16 respectively, so the molecular weight of carbon dioxide (CO_2) is $12 + 32 = 44$; 1 mol of carbon dioxide weighs 44 g so the total weight of carbon dioxide produced daily by a human being should be about $36 \times 44 = 1584$ g or around 1–2 kg.

Another (simpler) way is to estimate how much food you eat a day, since most foods have a similar composition to carbon dioxide. Glucose, for instance, has the chemical formula $C_6H_{12}O_6$ and so is 40 per cent carbon by weight, compared with carbon dioxide which is 27 per cent carbon. If you eat and metabolise 1 g of glucose you should therefore produce $1 \times 40/27 = 1.5$ g of carbon dioxide. So what is the dry weight of food you eat a day? Cornflakes, pasta and rice are some of the dry foods we eat (most foods contain only 5–30 per cent dry matter) and a pack of each usually contains 500 g. If (God forbid) you ate only cornflakes or spaghetti you might perhaps get through half to one packet a day, a weight of 250–500 g. Thus you would produce around 375–750 g carbon dioxide. Note that this estimate is somewhat smaller than the other one but is at least *of the same order of magnitude.*

2. The mass of carbon dioxide produced by the world's population will equal the mass per person multiplied by the number of people. Using the lower estimate for carbon dioxide production of 0.5 kg (many people in the world are starving):

$$\text{Human } CO_2 \text{ production} = 5 \times 10^9 \times 0.5 = 2\text{–}3 \times 10^9 \text{ kg day}^{-1}$$

Oil is composed largely of alkane hydrocarbons (C_nH_{2n+2}). Octane, for instance, is C_8H_{18} and 1 mol will burn to produce 8 mol of carbon dioxide. Therefore

114 g of octane will produce 352 g of carbon dioxide, so 1 g of fuel will produce about 3 g of carbon dioxide. Since

$$150 \times 10^6 \times 150 = 2.25 \times 10^{10} \text{ kg}$$

of fuel are burnt a day, the total amount of carbon dioxide produced will be $2.25 \times 10^{10} \times 3$ which equals around 7×10^{10} kg.

Human respiration produces about a thirtieth of the amount of carbon dioxide produced by fossil fuels. This could contribute significantly to global warming. However, much of our food is produced by crop plants which take up the carbon dioxide we expel.

Problem 3.2 1. After 20 years from 1994, the total carbon emissions from the factory will be $190 \times 20 = 3800$ t.

For each of the first 20 years (Table 3.1, column 1), work out the annual carbon fixation by 1 ha of forest, by interpolating values between those given for 5, 10 15 and 20 years (column 2). (For the first 5 years the increment is 0; for each following year it is $7/5 = 1.4$.) Then summate the amounts fixed in each of the 20 years (column 3) to give the total carbon fixation by each hectare over the first 20 years. Finally, divide the tonnes carbon emitted (3800) by the tonnes carbon fixed per hectare to give the number of hectares required to fix the total emission. The data are plotted in Fig. 3.1. (Note that 1 t ha^{-1} is equivalent to 0.1 kg m^{-2}.)

Tree age (years)	Annual fixation of C (t C ha^{-1} $year^{-1}$)	Cumulative fixation of C (t C ha^{-1})
1	0	0
2	0	0
3	0	0
4	0	0
5	0.2 (=0)	0.2
6	1.4	1.6
7	2.8	4.2
8	4.2	8.4
9	5.6	14.0
10	7.0	21.0
11	8.4	29.4
12	9.8	39.2
13	11.2	50.4
14	12.6	63.0
15	14.0	77.0
16	15.4	92.4
17	16.8	109.2
18	18.2	127.2
19	19.6	146.8
20	21.0	167.8

Table 3.3. The relationship between the age of the trees and the cumulative amount of carbon fixed.

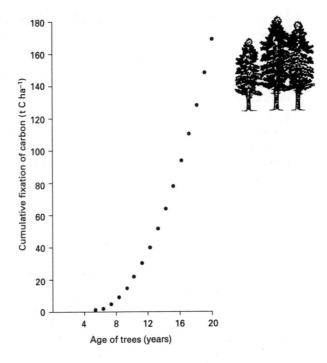

We can see that 1 ha of pine forest will have fixed 167.8 t of carbon when it is 20 years old. Thus to fix 3800 tonnes of carbon requires $3800/167.8 = 22.6$ ha of forest.

2.   Number of workers = 1/3 of 55 million = 18.3 million

Number of non-workers = 2/3 of 55 million = 36.7 million

so

18.3 million people each create $(190/100) = 1.9$ t year^{-1} carbon

36.7 million people each create $(1.9/4) = 0.475$ t year^{-1} carbon

Thus carbon emission by workers is

1.9×18.3 million = 34.8 million t year^{-1}

and carbon emission by non-workers is

0.475×36.7 million = 17.4 million t year^{-1}

Therefore

the total carbon emission by UK = 52.2 million t year^{-1}

= 1044 million t carbon in 20 years

In 20 years, 1 ha of pine forest will fix 167.8 t carbon, therefore 6.2 million ha (= 1044 million/167.8) of forest will be required. But 15 million ha are available. Thus $(6.2/15 \times 100) = 41.5$ per cent of available land would be required for pine forests.

Problem 3.3   1. (a)   In air, mucus production,

$$y = 24 \times 12.6 \times (7.237 \times 10^{-6} \times 38^{1.19}) = 0.17 \text{ g m}^{-2} \text{ day}^{-1}$$

(b)   In water, mucus production,

$$y = 24 \times 12.6 \times (8.51 \times 10^{-6} \times 38^{1.90}) = 0.26 \text{ g m}^{-2} \text{ day}^{-1}$$

2. In air,

$$y = (0.17 \times 365)/2 = 30 \text{ g m}^{-2} \text{ year}^{-1}$$

In water,

$$y = (0.26 \times 365)/2 = 47 \text{ g m}^{-2} \text{ year}^{-1}$$

Hence total mucus production $= 77 \text{ g m}^{-2} \text{ year}^{-1}$.

3. Yearly energy expenditure in mucus production is

$$8.98 \times 77.45 = 696 \text{ kJ m}^{-2} \text{ year}^{-1}$$

4. Let the mucus term, which has the value of 696 kJ m^{-2} year^{-1}, be M. How does this compare to Wright and Hartnoll's value? They estimated that mucus production was 8 per cent of assimilation, A, where

$$A = P_g + P_r + R + U$$

$$= 68 + 96 + 498 + 59$$

$$= 721 \text{ kJ m}^{-2} \text{ year}^{-1}.$$

Therefore their estimate of mucus production, M, was

$$M = 721 \times 0.08 = 57.7 \text{ kJ m}^{-2} \text{ year}^{-1}$$

Therefore, of their estimate of excretion of 59 kJ m^{-2} year^{-1}, they estimated that 57.7 kJ were due to mucus production. Therefore 1.3 kJ m^{-2} year^{-1} were due to other factors.

We can now work out the new energy budget:

$$C_s = P_g + P_r + R + F + U$$
$$= 68 + 96 + 498 + 884 + (1.3 + 696)$$
$$= 2244 \text{ kJ m}^{-2} \text{ year}^{-1}$$

The value of 2244 is much closer to Wright and Hartnoll's measure of consumption, C_m (2227), than their estimate, C_s (1605).

5. Energy assimilated is

$$\underset{P_g \quad P_r \quad R \quad U \quad M}{68 + 96 + 498 + 1 + 696} = 1359 \text{ kJ m}^{-2} \text{ year}^{-1}$$

Energy in mucus production $= 696 \text{ kJ m}^{-2} \text{ year}^{-1}$. Hence mucus production as a proportion of assimilated energy is $696/1359 = 51$ per cent.

Problem 3.4

1. (a) The maximum retention of nitrogen is obtained by multiplying the biomass by the nitrogen content (Table 3.4).
   (b) The throughput between each component can similarly be determined by multiplying the biomass throughput by the nitrogen content (Table 3.4). This calculation makes one major assumption: that the nitrogen content of the biomass which is cycled through the system has the same mean nitrogen concentration as the component from which it was derived. This may not be true for several reasons. For instance, trees tend to drop a higher proportion of foliage and small twigs which are high in nitrogen than large branches which are low in nitrogen. Therefore, the calculation gives a misleadingly low result for the throughput of aerial parts of the tree (5 kg ha^{-1}). The actual loss of nitrogen from aerial parts will be the same as the amount of nitrogen dropped on and lost from the forest floor, 14 kg ha^{-1}.

   Nitrogen might also be reabsorbed away from a component before its senescence, a sensible strategy which would might reduce nitrogen loss from the mycorrhizas and fungi.

2. The nitrogen cycle is shown in Fig. 3.2. It can be seen that only a relatively minor fraction of the total nitrogen cycling occurs because of growth of the aerial parts of

Table 3.4. The maximum retention of nitrogen and throughput between components in a Douglas fir ecosystem.

	Retention (kg ha^{-1})	Throughput (kg ha^{-1})
Aerial parts	416	5
Roots	39	0
Mycorrhizas	155	90
Forest floor	89	14
Fungi	184	74
Soil organic matter	7650	n.d.

n.d. = not determined.

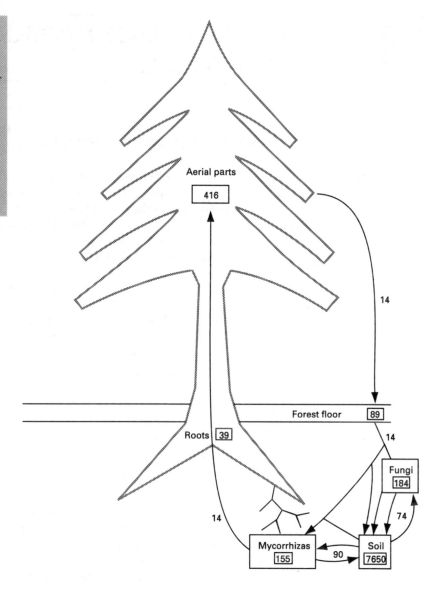

Figure 3.2. Nitrogen cycle for a Douglas fir forest ecosystem. Numbers in squares refer to the retention of nitrogen, numbers next to arrows to the throughput of nitrogen. Most nitrogen is in the soil, while most throughput is between the mycorrhizas and fungi and the soil.

the tree and the subsequent loss and decay of foliage (which are usually regarded as the main components of a terrestrial nitrogen cycle). It is impossible to be certain of the route taken by this nitrogen back into the tree. Some may have been leached directly through the soil to the mycorrhizas: the rest might have been broken down by fungi before incorporation into the soil.

Most of the cycling is actually due to the turnover and breakdown of mycorrhizas and fungi in the soil. Much of the nitrogen returned to the plant from the forest floor may also be cycled through fungi and soil before being returned via the mycorrhizas to the trees.

4

STABILITY AND DIVERSITY OF ECOSYSTEMS

Vegetation analysis from pollen data

Background   Different areas of the world's land surface are covered by different vegetation types. These have not always been there, however; vegetation has changed dramatically in the last 15 000 years both due to changes in climate which have occurred since the last ice age and to man's development of farming. The principal vegetation types in central North America are, from north to south, tundra, boreal conifer forest, parkland (grassland with scattered trees and shrubs), prairie and (eastwards) temperate broad-leaved forest. These vegetation types differ markedly in floristic composition, and hence produce very different mixtures of pollen grains. The pollen mixture falling to the ground within a uniform stand of a particular vegetation type can thus be used as a characteristic 'signature' defining that vegetation type. A simple sampling system for the signature is to extract the pollen grains incorporated into the topmost layers of the sediment laid down in a small lake within that vegetation type (a so-called 'surface sample').

Further reading

Miles (1978), Tallis (1991).

Data and questions   In the study reported below, 50 such surface samples were collected from a range of sites in central North America covering all five main vegetation types. The samples were analysed by a computer program (principal components analysis) to show their floristic similarities and differences, 'floristic composition' being measured as the proportions of the different pollen taxa present in the surface sample. The output of this analysis is shown in Fig. 4.1 as a two-dimensional plot of the relative positions of the 50 samples to portray their floristic similarity. Therefore two samples positioned close together are floristically similar, two samples far apart are floristically dissimilar. Individual samples from a given vegetation type have the same number on the plot.

The plot in Fig. 4.1 is divided into an arbitrary series of squares. The surface samples falling within some of these squares are characterised by high proportions of certain pollen taxa (shown on the plot); for example, the five samples in the top right-hand square have the highest values of *Betula* and Ericaceae pollen among the 50 samples (and, as might be expected, all come from the same vegetation type).

1. Deduce which samples come from which vegetation types.

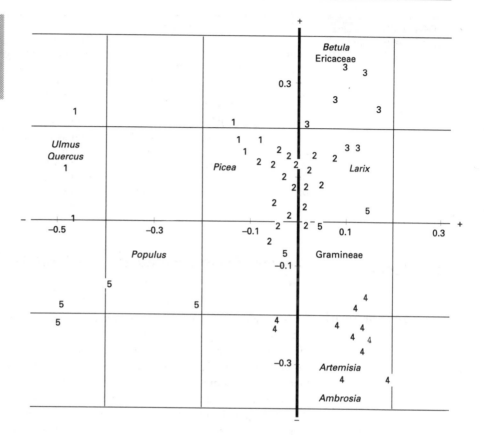

Samples from deeper layers in the sediments of the lakes also contained mixtures of pollen grains that originated from earlier plant communities at the site. These plant communities may or may not have been similar to the present-day ones. A series of sediment samples extending back in time about 10 000 years was collected from the two lakes, A and B, in south-central Canada, A being located 150 km north of B. From the pollen analyses of these samples a pollen diagram was drawn up for each site. Each pollen diagram was divided up into a number of zones (four in A, five in B), of relatively constant pollen composition. For each zone, the mean value of each pollen taxon present was calculated. The mean values of all the taxa present in a particular zone constitute a pollen 'signature', comparable to that represented by a modern surface sample, but of a much earlier date. The nine signatures so defined were compared by principal components analysis in the same way as the surface samples. Their coordinates on the plot in Fig. 4.1 are given in Table 4.1, together with the time periods covered by each zone.

2. Plot the positions of the nine zone signatures on Fig. 4.1 and use the total data set to deduce the vegetation history of the two sites, A and B. Comment on any differences shown and speculate on the significance of the differences.

| | Coordinates | | Time period |
Zone	X	Y	(thousand years ago)
A1	0.01	−0.09	8.5 to 7.7
A2	0.01	0.05	7.7 to 6.5
A3	0.05	0.11	6.5 to 2.8
A4	0.05	0.16	2.8 to 0.0
B1	−0.02	−0.17	11.0 to 10.7
B2	0.14	−0.23	10.7 to 9.5
B3	0.15	−0.16	9.5 to 6.4
B4	0.08	0.02	6.4 to 1.2
B5	0.03	0.08	1.2 to 0.0

Table 4.1. Coordinates of sediment samples.

Problem 4.2

Indices of biodiversity and similarity coefficients for moth faunas

Background   Environmental biologists often have to make decisions about the quality of habitats. A truly objective way of determining whether a particular habitat is a good one is therefore very important. Unfortunately, however, this is not very easy to do. Clearly, a good habitat would contain many species; however, it may also be important that there are large numbers of individuals of each species. Data about numbers of species and their abundance must therefore be combined to devise some 'index of diversity'. A number of biologists have therefore devised their own indices (see below), but since each stresses different aspects of the data, none will give a totally objective estimate of diversity.

It may also be important to determine how similar habitats are. Several 'similarity coefficients' have been devised to determine this, but again different coefficients stress different aspects of the data.

Despite the lack of any really objective assessment of habitat quality, both diversity and similarity coefficients are important tools of the environmental biologist. Familiarity with both the ways in which they are calculated and the particular biases of each method is essential.

William's index of diversity

This is denoted by α and is calculated from the equation

$$S = \alpha \ln(1 + (N/\alpha))$$

where S is the number of species and N the number of individuals.

Log series

The expected number of species represented by n specimens is

$$\alpha X^n/n, \text{ where } X = N/(N + \alpha).$$

Margalef's diversity index, I

$$I = (S - 1)/\ln N$$

Shannon's index, H'

$$H' = \Sigma p_i \ln p_i,$$

where p_i is the proportion of individuals in species i. There is a more convenient formula:

$$H' = \frac{N \ln N - \Sigma n_i \ln n_i}{N}$$

J'

A measure of relative diversity or evenness.

$$J' = H'/H'_{max}$$

where H'_{max} is the maximum possible diversity with S species, and $H'_{max} = \ln S$.

Jaccard's similarity coefficient, I

$$I = \frac{j}{a + b - j} \times 100$$

where j is the number of species occurring jointly in both communities, a the number of species in community a, and b the number of species in community b.

Sorensen's quotient of similarity, I

$$I = \frac{2j}{(a + b)} \times 100 \quad \text{(symbols as above)}$$

Mountford's index of similarity, I

$$I = \frac{2j}{2ab - (a + b)j} \times 1000 \quad \text{(symbols as above)}$$

Percentage similarity

The numbers of each species at both sites must first be converted into the percentage of all the individuals at a site which belong to each species. Then go through the list for the two sites and, where a species occurs in both sites, write down the *lower* percentage for each pair. Sum these percentages to find percentage similarity.

Further reading

Magurran (1988).

Species	F1	B1	F2	B2	Total
Beautiful golden Y	4	9	4	1	18
Small angleshades	2	1	0	4	7
Flame	3	3	3	3	12
Ingrailed clay	1	1	2	0	4
White ermine	0	2	1	0	2
Pale tussock	0	2	0	0	2
Common swift	0	0	0	2	2
Marbled minor	1	3	0	2	6
Dark arches	1	1	1	0	3
Purple clay	0	0	2	0	2
Green carpet	0	1	0	3	4
Silver ground carpet	2	1	0	1	4
Pretty chalk carpet	0	0	2	0	2
China mark	1	1	0	0	2
Pug (species?)	3	0	0	0	3
Small rivulet	2	0	0	0	2
Common marbled carpet	2	0	1	0	3
Singletons★	5	2	5	3	15
Number of individuals N	27	27	21	19	94
Number of species S	16	13	13	10	32

Table 4.2. Moths caught in mercury vapour traps on two nights (1 and 2) on front and back lawns (F and B) of Woodchester Park Cottage.

★ Moth species each represented by a single individual: Heart and dart, yellow underwing, flame shoulder, Hebrew character, poplar hawk, small elephant hawk, buff arches, alder, common wainscot, middle-barred minor, clouded-bordered brindle, riband wave, mottled beauty, Blomer's rivulet, garden carpet.

Data and questions

The following data refer to catches of moths in mercury vapour traps at two sites at Woodchester Park, Gloucestershire, England in early July.

1. Use the data in Table 4.2 to calculate Williams's diversity index, α, for the total catch, and compare the numbers of individuals in each species with the expected log distribution.

2. Next, calculate Williams's, Margalef's and Shannon's indices for moth diversity for the first night on the front lawn (F1). Insert your data into Table 4.3 which shows these indices for the other three trapping events, and compare the ranking obtained using the three methods.

3. Finally, calculate the similarity of the moth faunas trapped on the front and back lawns on the first night, using Jaccard's, Sorensen's and Mountford's similarity

	α	Margalef	H'	J' (as %)
F1	?	?	?	?
F2	13.0	3.9	2.4	94.6
B1	9.9	3.6	2.2	86.4
B2	8.5	3.1	2.2	93.8

Table 4.3. Diversity indices of different moth samples.

Comparison between:	Jaccard	Sorensen	Mountford	% similarity
F1 and B1	?	?	?	?
F1 and F2	23.8	34.5	36.9	38.1
F1 and B2	16.1	38.5	52.6	37.8
F2 and B1	18.2	38.5	48.1	42.3
F2 and B2	9.5	17.4	18.7	19.6
B1 and B2	35.3	52.2	98.4	38.0

Table 4.4. Similarly coefficients of different moth samples.

coefficients and the percentage similarity. Add your results to those in Table 4.4. Which are the most and least similar sites?

Problem 4.3

Mark–release–recapture of wood crickets

Background Plants and many sessile animals can be sampled using static sampling techniques (quadrats, transects, etc.), but these techniques are not useful for mobile animals. The mark–release–recapture technique is commonly used for these animals. If you have not met this before, ask yourself the following question.

You have a black bag containing an unknown number of marbles (or sweets). You remove 10 marbles, put a mark on each one, put them back in the bag, and shake the bag to mix the marked and unmarked marbles. Then take out 8 marbles. If 4 of those 8 marbles are marked, how many marbles were in the bag at the start?

The answer is most probably 20, because if your sample contains 50 per cent marked marbles, and you know that 10 marbles have marks, then the same number, another 10, must be unmarked, $10 + 10 = 20$. We have to say 'most probably', because it would be quite possible to pull out a different proportion of marked and unmarked marbles. If we are dealing with a bigger 'population' then our estimates become more reliable, provided that the marked ones are thoroughly mixed with the remainder before sampling, that the marks do not come off, and that marking does not make a marble any more or less likely to be chosen. Formally, this estimate of population size is known as the Lincoln index.

The Lincoln index, LI

$$LI_1 = \frac{n_1 \times n_2}{m_2}$$

where LI_1 is the estimate of population on the first day, n_1 the number caught on the first day, n_2 the number caught on the second day and m_2 the number marked on the first day and recaptured on the second day. In the example above, $n_1 = 10$, $n_2 = 8$ and $m_2 = 4$, thus $LI_1 = 20$. The Lincoln index assumes that marked individuals mix evenly with the rest, do not lose their marks (e.g. by moulting) and behave exactly like unmarked ones (being no more or less prone to predation or capture). It also assumes that there is no influx of unmarked individuals by birth or immigration.

Jolly's method

Jolly's and Manly and Parr's methods of estimating population size require at least 3 days of captures. These methods involve the idea of estimating the number of animals available for capture on the second day, but which avoid capture (i.e. the numbers caught on the first and third day, but not the second day): this is called Z_2. This method compensates for animals entering or leaving the population.

Jolly's method starts with the construction of a trellis. The numbers in the trellis (15, 10 and 20 in this example) are entered according to the day last seen, i.e. 15 animals caught on day 2 have the mark from day 1, 10 caught on day 3 only have the mark from day 1, 20 caught on day 3 have the day 2 mark (regardless of whether or not they have a day 1 mark).

	Population sample size n_i	Marked animals from day 1	Marked animals from day 2	Marked animals
Day 1	30			
Day 2	35	15		$\rightarrow m_2 = 15$
Day 3	40	$10 = Z_2$	20	$\rightarrow m_3 = 30$
Recapture of marked animals		$\rightarrow R_1 = 25$	$R_2 = 20$	

Here, Z_2 are the animals available for capture on day 2 which avoid capture, i.e. the 10 animals caught on days 1 and 3 but not on day 2, i.e. $Z_2 = 10$.

The estimate of the population on the second day, P_2, is

$$P_2 = \frac{n_2 \times M_2}{m_2}$$

where M_2 is an estimate of the marked animals available for capture on day 2, which can be estimated knowing Z_2, the number of animals caught on days 1 and 3 but not on day 2:

$$M_2 = \frac{n_2 \times Z_2}{R_2} + m_2$$

R_2, Z_2 and m_2 are obtained from the trellis.

In this example

$$n_2 = 35 \qquad R_2 = 20 \qquad Z_2 = 10 \quad \text{and} \quad m_2 = 15,$$

so

$$M_2 = [(35 \times 10)/20] + 15 = 32.5$$

Therefore

$$P_2 = (35 \times 32.5)/15 = 76$$

Manly and Parr's method

The basis of this method is that the best estimate of the population on day 2 is the total number caught that day multiplied by the sampling fraction (the numbers available to be caught divided by the numbers actually caught). The animals caught each day are recorded on a table, where x = animals found that day, y = animals found that day and the day before and after, and z = animals not found that day but found before and after (so were available to be caught). As animals are recaptured on subsequent days, the earlier lines of the table are altered. It looks complicated, but is easy in practice.

20 animals were found on day 1:

	Day 1	Day 2	Day 3
20	x		

On day 2, 30 unmarked animals and 5 marked animals were found. The 5 animals found on days 1 and 2 reduces the total for the first row to 15:

15	x		
5	x	x	
30		x	

On day 3, 27 animals were found: 15 unmarked, together with 2 marked on the first day, 8 marked on the second day, and 2 marked on both the first and the second days.
  The 2 animals found on days 1 and 3 reduce the 15 to 13:

13	x		
5	x	x	
30		x	
15			x
2	x	z	x

(The z indicates the animals must have been there but not caught on day 2.)

The 8 animals found on days 2 and 3 reduce the 30 to 22:

13	x		
5	x	x	
22		x	
2	x	z	x
8		x	x
15			x
2	x	y	x

(The y represents an x with x's on both sides.)

The 2 animals found on days 1, 2 and 3 reduce the 5 to 3, so the table finally looks like this:

	Day 1	Day 2	Day 3
13	x		
3	x	x	
22		x	
2	x	z	x
8		x	x
15			x
2	x	y	x

The estimate of the population on the second day, P_2, is

$$P_2 = n_2 \times \frac{\Sigma y + \Sigma z}{\Sigma y}$$

where $(\Sigma y + \Sigma z)/\Sigma y$ is the sampling fraction. In the table above, $\Sigma y = 2$ and $\Sigma z = 2$, so the sampling fraction is 2. The number caught on the second day was 35, so $P_2 = 70$.

Further reading

Begon (1979).

Data and questions

The data refer to captures and recaptures of wood crickets, *Nemobius sylvestris*, on 3 successive days in a marked out area of 14 × 14 m just inside an oakwood in southern France. On the first day, all wood crickets caught by 20 students in 1 hour were placed into four containers, and a record kept of the numbers caught. At the end of the sampling, the wood crickets were narcotised with carbon dioxide and marked on the prothorax with a small dab of red paint. They were then allowed to recover and released at four sites within the area. On the first day 487 wood crickets were caught, marked and released.

The next day, all the wood crickets in the same area of woodland were again captured in 1 hour, by the same group of students. The numbers of unmarked and red-marked wood crickets caught were recorded separately: 154 wood crickets with red marks, and 438 wood crickets with no paint marks, a total of 592, were found on the second day. At the end of sampling, all the wood crickets were narcotised, marked with blue paint and released.

On the third and final day, the students again collected for 1 hour in the same area, and recorded separately the numbers of wood crickets with different paint marks. A total of 314 wood crickets were collected: 171 with no paint marks, 32 with only red paint marks, 91 with only blue paint marks, and 20 with both red and blue paint marks. The wood crickets were then released.

1. Calculate the total population of wood crickets present on the second day using (a) the Lincoln index, (b) Jolly's method, and (c) Manly and Parr's technique, from the guides provided.

2. Comment on the limitations of these techniques of estimating abundance.

3. Which of the following species would be most suitable for mark–release–recapture estimations of sample size, and what time interval would you allow? (a) Aphid, (b) garden snail, (c) woodlouse, (d) grasshopper, (e) limpet, (f) shore crab.

Problem 4.4   Plant succession

Background   The botanical composition of an area of land is rarely stable, particularly in habitats which are affected by man. Newly forming land, such as that of salt marshes and sand dunes, may be colonised by pioneering plants which modify the habitat so that other species can colonise and subsequently outcompete them. The pattern of vegetation change which results is known as a 'primary succession'. A similar process occurs when existing land is cleared: species colonise from surrounding areas and the composition of the vegetation gradually changes in what is known as a 'secondary succession' before a stable 'climax vegetation' may be reached. Interference by man can interrupt or alter this process.

Further reading

Begon *et al.* (1986: Ch. 16), Krebs (1994: Ch. 22).

Data and questions   Figure 4.2 shows the pattern of the relative abundance of plant species at different times after fields were abandoned in southern Illinois, USA. Figure 4.3 shows the pattern of the relative abundance of plant species in an experimental plot of permanent pasture at Rothamsted, England, following the start of continuous applications of nitrogen fertiliser.

1. Interpret the pattern of vegetation change described by Fig. 4.2. How does the diversity of plants in the fields change over time and why?

2. Describe the change in the life-history strategies of the plant species on the site. Why does this occur?

3. How do you expect the vegetation to change after greater lengths of time? Sketch the relative abundance of species after 200 years.

4. Interpret the pattern of vegetation change described by Fig. 4.3. How has the diversity of plants in the plot changed over time and why?

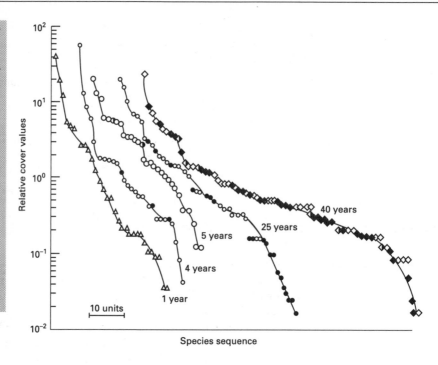

Figure 4.2. Patterns of the relative abundance of species at five different stages of abandonment in old fields in southern Illinois. The patterns are expressed as the percentage that a given species contributes to the total area covered by all species in a community, plotted against the species rank and ordered from most to least abundant. The symbols are open for herbs, half open for shrubs and closed for trees (from May, 1985).

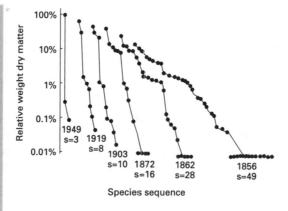

Figure 4.3. Changes in the patterns of relative abundance of species in an experimental plot of permanent pasture at Parkgrass, Rothamsted, England, following continuous application of nitrogen fertiliser, starting in 1856. (Species with abundance less than 0.01 per cent were recorded as 0.01 per cent.) (From May, 1985.)

5. In recent times 'set–aside' policies have seen increasing areas of agricultural land taken out of production. It is hoped that one result of these policies is to increase the biodiversity of these areas.

   Using the information given in these examples and your botanical knowledge, comment on the likely effectiveness of set-aside policies (in which land is left fallow for up to 5 years) in botanical conservation.

Problem 4.5 — Distribution of dog's mercury

Background

With the retreat of glaciers after the last ice age much of northern Europe and the eastern USA became covered in broad-leaved woodland. These woodlands had a diverse flora of understorey herbs and other plants as well as a diverse fauna. The vegetation would be the same today were it not for man, who started clearing Europe in neolithic times and America much more recently, to make way for farming. Only small patches of woodland remain, usually much managed by man, so it is difficult to determine whether a particular wood has always been there and so is a remnant of the 'ancient woodland' or whether it is a 'secondary wood', having been replanted some time after the land was cleared. To help in the identification, landscape historians have tried to identify certain 'indicator species' which are characteristic only of ancient woodland. Such species should be unable to survive in open country between woods and should be poor colonisers of new areas.

Further reading

Begon *et al.* (1986: Ch. 20), Rackham (1986), Williamson (1981), Peterken and Game (1981).

Data and questions

Dog's mercury *Mercurialis perennis*, is a shade-tolerant perennial herb which cannot survive in open country. It has been suggested that *Mercurialis* may be used as an indicator species for ancient woodland. In a survey carried out in Lincolnshire, England, in the late 1970s, *Mercurialis* was found in 57 of the 87 'ancient' woods

Wistman's wood, Dartmoor, England. This oak-dominated wood is thought to be one of the few surviving remnants of unmanaged ancient woodland in Britain. The trees are small and stunted but provide shelfter for a great diversity of mosses, lichens, herbs, shrubs, invertebrates and woodland birds.

Dog's Mercury, *Mercurialis perennis*, a perennial woodland herb which, because of its poor colonising ability, may be used as an indicator of ancient woodland in Northern Europe

which had existed for at least the past 400 years compared with 51 of the 213 'secondary' woods that maps and records showed had been planted in the last 400 years.

1. How would you determine whether there is a *significant* difference in the distribution of *Mercurialis* between ancient and secondary woods?

2. Suggest how *Mercurialis* has come to be present in the secondary woods.

3. Of the 47 woods planted between 1820 and 1887 (when Ordnance Survey maps of the area were produced) 10 had been colonised by *Mercurialis* but only one of the 64 woods planted since 1887. What does this tell you about the colonising ability of *Mercurialis*?

Table 4.5 shows the number of these secondary woods of different sizes and degrees of isolation within the study area in which *Mercurialis* is present or absent (bracketed numbers).

4. Plot two graphs showing the effect of (a) area and (b) isolation on the presence of *Mercurialis*. Comment on these results in the light of your knowledge of biogeography.

Figure 4.4 shows the relationship between the proportion of woods containing *Mercurialis* and the number of other species of shade-tolerant herbs in both 'ancient' and 'secondary' woods.

5. What do these findings imply about the ecology of ancient and secondary woods and the biology of *Mercurialis*?

Table 4.5. The number of secondary woods planted between 1820 and 1887 of different size and degree of isolation which contain *Mercurialis*. Numbers in brackets indicate woods without *Mercurialis*.

Distance from woods with *Mercurialis* (km) up to:	Area (ha) up to:						
	0.1	0.3	1.0	3.0	10	30	Total
0.1			1			1	2
0.2			1		1		2
0.4			1(1)	1			2(1)
0.8			(2)	(1)	1		1(3)
1.6		(2)	(1)	(1)	(4)	2	2(8)
3.2			(3)	(9)	1(7)		1(19)
6.4			(3)	(2)	(1)		(6)
Total		(2)	3(10)	1(13)	3(12)	3	10(37)

Figure 4.4. The relationship between the proportion of woods containing *Mercurialis* and the number of shade-tolerating herbs in two categories of wood: ancient and secondary. The number of woods in each sample is shown above the points. The range of numbers of species of shade-tolerating herbs has been divided into classes of ten species (e.g. 0 to 10, 10 to 20). (After Peterken and Game, 1981.)

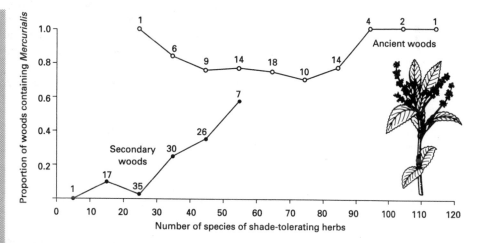

SOLUTIONS

Problem 4.1

1. It is best to start by making the most obvious deductions. Sample 4 is clearly from prairie, as it contains the herbs *Artemisia* and *Ambrosia* which are characteristic of this vegetation type, along with some grasses. Sample 3 is from tundra, as it contains both *Betula* (birch) and Ericaceae (heathers) which are tundra species. Sample 2 is boreal conifer forest, since the conifer species *Picea* (spruce) and *Larix* (larch) are both present.

It is slightly more difficult to decide about the last two samples since their plots are rather more scattered on the diagram. However, sample 1 is the only one in which the long-lived broad-leaved trees, *Ulmus* (elm) and *Quercus* (oak) are present. Therefore sample 1 is probably from the broad-leaved forest. Similarly sample 5 may contain a mixture of both Graminae (grasses) and *Populus* (poplars) which are trees which survive well in open parkland as many species such as aspen are quite drought resistant.

Therefore the samples are from the following vegetation types:

      Sample 1   Temperate broad-leaved forest
      Sample 2   Boreal conifer forest
      Sample 3   Tundra
      Sample 4   Prairie
      Sample 5   Parkland

2. The zone signatures of the nine samples are plotted in Fig. 4.5. At site A, the vegetation seems to be changing from parkland to conifer forest and finally to be on the verge of becoming tundra. At site B, in contrast, the vegetation seems initially to be changing from parkland to prairie. The process is then reversed and the site gradually is taken over by parkland and finally conifer forest. Both of these vegetation changes are probably due to a gradual cooling of this region which seems to have been going on for the last 10 000 years. Prairie is characteristic of a warmer, drier climate than parkland or conifer forest, and tundra is found in colder regions. In both sites, therefore, the vegetation has been changing over the last 10 000 years to that characteristic of cooler regions.

There are noticeable differences between the two sites at the same time period. From around 9000 to 6000 years ago, when site A is changing from parkland to conifer forest, B is still dominated by prairie. Likewise, when B is changing to conifer forest, from 6000 years ago till the present, A is becoming tundra. These differences are related to the geographical position of the two sites: A is 150 km north of B and is therefore probably colder. At any given time, therefore, its vegetation would be characteristic of cooler regions.

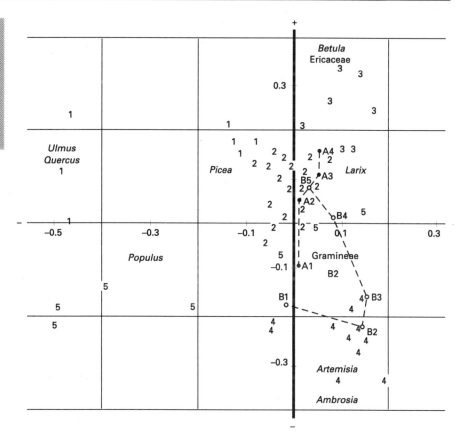

Fig. 4.5. Principal components analysis of pollen samples from two sites in south-central Canada, showing vegetation changes over the last 10 000 years.

Problem 4.2   1. **Calculation of Williams's index of diversity for the total catch.** The index α must be worked out by a series of approximations. Start by assuming $\alpha = 10$, then increase it if the right-hand side is smaller than S, and vice versa.

$$32 = 10 \ln[1 + (94/10)] = 10 \ln(10.4) = 10 \times 2.34 = 23.4$$
Too small!
Try $20{:}32 = 20 \ln[1 + (94/20)] = 20 \ln(5.7) = 20 \times 1.74 = 34.8$
Too big!
Try $17{:}32 = 17 \ln[1 + (94/17)] = 17 \ln(6.5) = 17 \times 1.88 = 31.9$
Too small!
Try $17.5{:}32 = 17.5 \ln[1 + (94/17.5)] = 17.5 \ln(6.4) = 17.5 \times 1.85 = 32.4$
Too big!
Try $17.1{:}32 = 17.1 \ln[1 + (94/17.1)] = 17.1 \ln(6.5) = 17.1 \times 1.9 = 32.0$
O.K.! $\alpha = 17.1$

Since $\alpha = 17.1$, then $X = 94/(94 + 17.1) = 0.846$.

69

So the expected and observed number of species represented by 1, 2, 3, 4, 5, 6, or more specimens is as follows:

Number of specimens	Expected number of species	Observed number of species
1	$\alpha X = 14.5$	15
2	$\alpha X^2/2 = 6.1$	6
3	$\alpha X^3/3 = 3.5$	4
4	$\alpha X^4/4 = 2.2$	3
5	$\alpha X^5/5 = 1.5$	0
6	$\alpha X^6/6 = 1.0$	1
>6	$32 - (14.5 + 6.1 + 3.5 + 2.2 + 1.5 + 1) = 5.5$	3

2. **Calculation of different diversity indices for sample F1, and comparison of methods.** Williams's index for F1 is 16.5, calculated as follows: $S = 16$, $N = 27$.

Try $\alpha = 10:16 = 10 \ln[1 + (27/10)] = 10 \times 1.31 = 13.1$ Too small!
Try $\alpha = 15:16 = 15 \ln[1 + (27/15)] = 15 \times 1.03 = 15.4$ Nearly!
Try $\alpha = 16:16 = 16 \ln[1 + (27/16)] = 16 \times 0.99 = 15.8$ Very nearly!
Try $\alpha = 16.5:16 = 16.5 \ln[1 + (27/16.5)] = 16.5 \times 0.97 = 16$ O.K.!

Margalef's index for F1 is 4.6, calculated as follows:

$$I = (16 - 1)/(\ln 27) = 17/3.3 = 4.55 \approx 4.6$$

Shannon's H' is 2.6 calculated as follows. Sample F1 has 27 individuals of 16 species represented by 4, 2, 3, 1, 1, 1, 2, 1, 3, 2, 2, 1, 1, 1, 1, 1 individuals.

$H' = [27 \ln 27 - (4 \ln 4 + 2 \ln 2 + 3 \ln 3 + 1 \ln 1 + 1 \ln 1 + 1 \ln 1$
$+ 2 \ln 2 + 1 \ln 1 + 3 \ln 3 + 2 \ln 2 + 2 \ln 2 + 1 \ln 1 + 1 \ln 1 + 1 \ln 1$
$+ 1 \ln 1 + 1 \ln 1)]/16.$

Now $1 \ln 1$ is zero, so this becomes

$H' = [27 \ln 27 - (4 \ln 4 + 2 \ln 2 + 3 \ln 3 + 2 \ln 2 + 3 \ln 3 + 2 \ln 2$
$+ 2 \ln 2)]/27$
$= [88.99 - (5.55 + 1.39 + 3.30 + 1.39 + 3.30 + 1.39 + 1.39)]/16$
$H' = (88.99 - 17.71)/27 = 2.64$

$H'_{max} = \ln 16 = 2.773$, so
$J' = 2.64/2.773 = 0.953$ or 95.3 per cent

Hence the table below can be filled in as follows:

	α	Margalef	H'	J' (as %)
F1	16.5	4.6	2.6	95.3
F2	13.0	3.9	2.4	94.6
B1	9.9	3.6	2.2	86.4
B2	8.5	3.1	2.2	93.8

The three methods rank the four samples in the same order, from F1 (most diverse) to B2 (least diverse).

3. **Similarity of samples F1 and B1**
    (a) Jaccard's similarity coefficient, I: there are sixteen species in F1 and 13 in B1: eight species are found in both samples. Hence

    $$I = 8/(16 + 13 - 8) = 0.381 \text{ or } 38.1 \text{ per cent}$$

    (b) Sorensen's quotient of similarity, I

    $$I = [(2 \times 8)/(16 + 13)] \times 100 = 55.2 \text{ per cent}$$

    (c) Mountford's index of similarity, I

    $$I = ((2 \times 8)/\{(2 \times 16 \times 13) - [(16 + 13) \times 8]\}) \times 1000$$
    $$= [16/(416 - 232)] \times 1000 = 87.0 \text{ per cent}$$

    (d) Percentage similarity. In Table 4.6, we can ignore species which occur in only one of the two samples. For the remaining eight species the *lower* percentage is underlined. The underlined values are then added up to give the percentage similarity as follows:

    $$14.8 + 3.7 + 11.1 + 3.7 + 3.7 + 3.7 + 3.7 + 3.7 = 48.1 \text{ per cent}$$

These values can be included in Table 4.4 as in Table 4.7.

Table 4.6. Percentage of all moths caught at each site which belong to each species. Based on data in Table 4.2.

	F1	B1
Beautiful golden Y	14.8	33.3
Small angleshades	7.4	3.7
Flame	11.1	11.1
Ingrailed clay	3.7	3.7
White ermine	0	7.4
Pale tussock	0	7.4
Marbled minor	3.7	11.1
Dark arches	3.7	3.7
Green carpet	0	3.7
Silver ground carpet	7.4	3.7
China mark	3.7	3.7
Pug (species?)	11.1	0
Small rivulet	7.4	0
Common marbled carpet	7.4	0

Table 4.7. Similarity coefficients of different moth samples.

Comparison between:	Jaccard	Sorensen	Mountford	% similarity
F1 and B1	38.1	55.2	87.0	48.1
F1 and F2	23.8	34.5	36.9	38.1
F1 and B2	16.1	38.5	52.6	37.8
F2 and B1	18.2	38.5	48.1	42.3
F2 and B2	9.5	17.4	18.7	19.6
B1 and B2	35.3	52.2	98.4	38.0

In Table 4.7 it can be seen that F2 and B2 are the least similar samples in all four tests, and three of the four tests show F1 and B1 to be the most similar.

Problem 4.3   1. (a)   The Lincoln index for the second day, LI_2, is

$$\frac{\text{Number caught on day 2} \times \text{number caught on day 3}}{\text{Numbers marked on day 2 and recaptured on day 3}}$$

$$= \frac{(592 \times 314)}{111} = 1675$$

Note: numbers recaptured include those with blue marks only and with blue and red marks, i.e. $91 + 20 = 111$.

(b)   Jolly's estimate of the population on day 2:

	n	d_1			
Day 1	487				
Day 2	592	154	d_2	$\rightarrow$	$m_2 = 154$
Day 3	314	$32 = Z_2$	111	$\rightarrow$	$m_3 = 133$

	R_1	R_2
	186	111

$$Z_2 = 32$$
$$M_2 = [(592 \times 32)/111] + 154 = 324.7$$
$$P_2 = (592 \times 324.7)/154 = 1248$$

(c)   Manly and Parr's estimation of the population on day 2:

	Day 1	Day 2	Day 3
$301 \leftarrow \cancel{333} \leftarrow \cancel{487}$	x		
$134 \leftarrow (-20)\ \cancel{154}$	x	x	
$347 \leftarrow \cancel{438}$		x	
32	x	z	x
91		x	x
171			x
20	x	y	x

$$P_2 = n_2 \times \frac{\Sigma y + \Sigma z}{\Sigma y}$$

$$= 592 \times [(20 + 32)/20]$$
$$= 1539$$

2. (a) The Lincoln index makes no allowance for influx or efflux of animals.

   (b) The paint makes marked individuals more visible and more likely to be recaptured.

   (c) The handling may reduce the viability of marked animals (certainly many wood crickets with less than six legs were recaptured).

3. (a) Aphids have a fixed position and a short life span, so MRR techniques are unsuitable.

   (b) Snails are slow moving, and most active on moist nights, so a longer period is needed to allow mixing of the population, especially during dry periods.

   (c) Woodlice moult their skins regularly so marks will be lost. Therefore the technique would overestimate the population and would be unsuitable if the survey was carried out over long time periods.

   (d) Grasshoppers can be estimated well with the technique, but only if they are adult and have therefore stopped moulting.

   (e) Limpet populations from the upper shore regularly return ('home') to their home scar. Therefore no apparent mixing would take place and the technique would be unsuitable.

   (f) Shore crabs are unsuitable because the onshore population which we are sampling mixes with the very much larger offshore population.

Problem 4.4

1. After abandonment a field first becomes colonised by a few plant species, of which one or two are very dominant. As time goes by, however, more species colonise the site and the most numerous species become less dominant. The diversity of species, therefore, increases: both because there are more species and because the species are more equitably distributed. The increase in diversity probably occurs because the pioneer species change the habitat, altering the nutrient and water status of the soil and providing variable shade. This produces a range of microhabitats for which different species are adapted. As these colonise, environmental heterogeneity is further increased and further colonisation occurs.

2. The fields will be colonised initially by annual and biennial plant species, which tend to have small, mobile seeds and have fast growth rates. After a few years, however, these will start to be outcompeted by perennial herbs which have a permanent rootstock or produce bulbs. This gives the perennials a competitive advantage because both roots and shoots can be produced faster at the start of each season, allowing them to outcompete annuals for nutrients and water as well as light. After 15–25 years the perennials themselves start to be replaced by shrubs and trees which are initially slow-growing, but produce a permanent above-ground structure. As a result the shrubs and trees start to shade the perennials and to replace them. These results therefore seem to describe a typical 'plant succession'.

3. After greater lengths of time one would expect the tree species to become more dominant as they grow taller and shade out the herbaceous vegetation. In time the faster-growing pioneer trees, such as aspen and birch, will themselves be

outcompeted by climax species such as oak and beech which cast denser shade. Eventually the diversity of the field will fall again as the vegetation becomes dominated by the climax tree species and the few herbaceous and shrub species which can survive in the dark beneath the canopy. After 200 years the graph of relative abundance would be rather like that after 1 year. Diversity of ecosystems is often maximised by 'intermediate' rates of disturbance. However, if the rainfall was low the succession might not carry on to its climax; it may be too dry for a canopy to develop and the field would start to resemble undisturbed prairie.

4. Addition of high levels of nitrogen fertiliser causes the number of species to fall as fewer and fewer species take over and become dominant. The diversity drops dramatically because selection favours only those species with fast growth rates under conditions of high nitrogen. The heterogeneity of the habitat drops and with it the diversity as the favoured species outcompete all the others.

5. After 5 years land will only have been colonised by a small fraction of the number of species it would support if left fallow for many years. Those species which do colonise fallow land also tend to be common species of annuals and perennials, such as ragwort *Senecio vulgaris*, docks and thistles: plants which colonise and do well on recently disturbed ground. There will be very few of the rarer slow-growing but long-lived perennials characteristic of settled and more diverse habitats. The scheme will have little conservation value.

Problem 4.5

1. To determine whether there is a significant difference the best test to use is the Chi-squared test. First, construct the contingency tables for observed and expected values.

Type of wood	Presence		Total
	Present	Absent	
Ancient	57 (31.3)	30 (55.7)	87
Secondary	51 (76.7)	162 (136.3)	213
Total	108	192	300

Chi-squared is then equal to $\Sigma[(O - E)^2/E]$. In this case

$$\text{Chi-squared} = 21.1 + 11.9 + 8.6 + 4.8 = 46.4$$

There is a significant difference at the 0.1 per cent level.

2. Since *Mercurialis* cannot survive in open country, the plants in secondary woods must have colonised the sites from older woods. It is unlikely that this could have been achieved by vegetative reproduction (though *Mercurialis* can spread by use of rhizomes); it is far more likely to have occurred by dispersal of seeds which can survive in open country. Alternatively it might have survived in hedgerows.

3. New woods seem to be colonised only very slowly. This tells us that the efficiency of seed dispersal, or maybe survival and germination of seeds, is very low. *Mercurialis* is a poor coloniser.

4. Figure 4.6 shows that there is a somewhat weak relationship between presence of *Mercurialis* and wood area: the larger the wood, the more likely *Mercurialis* is to be present. Figure 4.7 shows a stronger relationship with isolation: more isolated woods are less likely to contain *Mercurialis*. These results are both consistent with current theories about diversity of island populations (see Begon *et al.* 1986). Large 'islands' and ones nearest the 'mainland' should have larger numbers of species than small, distant islands because they are more likely to be colonised. Since large woods can support larger populations, the chances of a species becoming extinct there are also lower.

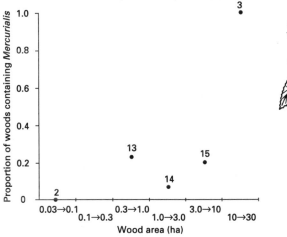

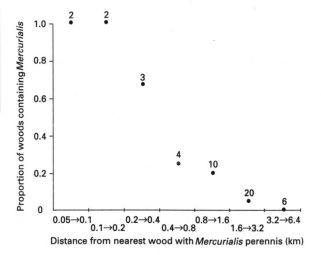

5. Figure 4.4 shows that ancient woods tend to contain more species of herbs than secondary ones. Their higher diversity, which gives ancient woods higher conservation value, is because plants have had much longer to colonise them and because they are the remains of much larger stretches of woodland which could support large numbers of species. The figure also shows that in ancient woods the incidence of *Mercurialis* is uncorrelated with the number of species; it is almost always present. This suggests that *Mercurialis* is an unusually persistent plant which can survive even in small, isolated or unsuitable woods where other species have become extinct.

In secondary woods the incidence of *Mercurialis* is strongly correlated with the number of other species present. This is probably related to colonisation; if *Mercurialis*, a poor coloniser, has reached a wood so will have other species. The woods with few species present are probably small, isolated woods which have only been recently planted.

SECTION

3

HUMAN IMPACTS

5

OVER-EXPLOITATION OF RESOURCES

Logging and soil erosion

Background   Recent years have seen the unprecedented destruction of both tropical and temperate rainforest by logging for the valuable timber and clearance of land for agriculture. In Borneo, East Malaysia, logging predominates since the population is small and concentrated in towns around the coast. One of the many bad effects of logging activities in tropical rainforests is that bare soil is exposed. It has been suggested that this may result in erosion by heavy tropical storms, soil being washed into the rivers which drain the area. This is currently being investigated in many parts of the world.

Further reading

Wild (1993: Ch. 12), Morgan (1986).

Data and questions   Hydrological studies being carried out in the Danum Valley field centre in Sabah, Malaysia have attempted to determine the size of the problem. The river Segama, which drains a heavily logged area of 3000 km^2, was monitored during 1992 over the entire range of conditions, from the low river levels recorded during drought to the high levels which occur when the river is in spate following heavy tropical storms. The manner in which the discharge of water in the channel and the sediment concentration vary as the height of the river changes is shown in Figs 5.1 and 5.2. (The average soil density is 1.4×10^3 kg m^{-3}).

1. What measurements had to be taken to determine the discharge of water?

2. Plot a graph showing how the rate at which sediment is discharged varies with the level of the river. What is the rate of sediment discharge at a river level of 4 m?

3. Water levels were recorded every 2 hours over a 28-hour period on 8–9 August 1992 following a storm in which 32 mm of rain fell (Fig. 5.3). Use the information to calculate the total amount of sediment washed down the river during this time.

4. On average what depth of soil was eroded by the storm? Is this loss significant?

5. What other harmful effects might result from the heavy sediment load (the river *looked* extremely muddy)?

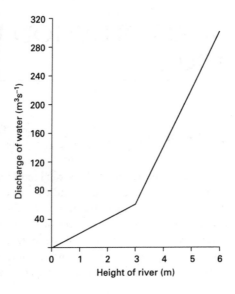

Figure 5.1. The relationship between the height of the Segama river and its rate of discharge of water.

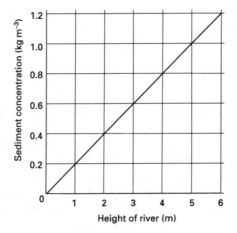

Figure 5.2. The relationship between the height of the Segama river and the sediment concentration of the water.

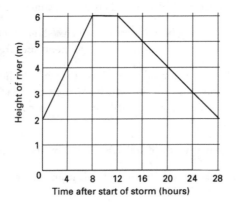

Figure 5.3. The change in height of the river Segama following a storm on 8–9 August 1992.

Field experiments were also carried out during the storm, measuring the runoff of soil from small plots of bare ground. Each plot measured 20 × 2 m and it was found that on average 90 kg of soil was lost from each experimental plot.

6. Calculate the depth of soil lost from each plot. Comment on the differences in the results obtained by the two methods.

Problem 5.2	**Sheep grazing and moorland regeneration**

Background The moorlands of upland regions of northern Europe appear to be natural ecosystems. In fact, most are the result of deforestation and have been extensively managed, either for the grazing of sheep and goats or for game birds. Traditionally there is a cycle of heather burning followed by the regeneration of new shoots.

It has been suggested that overgrazing by sheep on the upland moors of northern England has prevented natural regeneration of heather and resulted both in a significant reduction in the ground cover and erosion of peat. Attempts are now being made to restore the vegetation by reducing grazing pressure.

Further reading

Anderson and Yalden (1981), Usher and Thompson (1988).

Peat erosion at Cold Harbour Moor in the southern pennines. Overgrazing by sheep has caused loss of heather cover, and peat is being removed by the action of wind and rain right down to the bedrock. Here only a few 'peat hags' remain, seen in the foreground and on the skyline.

Data and questions The following data (Table 5.1) relate to field trials carried out in the southern Pennines on the effects of sheep grazing on the establishment of heather plants on bare moorland areas. Heather seed was supplied to experimental areas protected by sheep-proof fences (A) and to comparable unfenced areas (B). The trials were started in 1980 and the established heather plants flowered for the first time in autumn 1983. Various measures of heather performance were made over the 3 years, and are summarised in Table 5.1.

1–7. What aspects of the establishment process are being assessed by the different measures 1–7 in Table 5.1, and how are they affected by the grazing?

8. How might the measures be combined to derive a quantitative estimate of the impact of sheep grazing on the establishment of heather in the trial plots over the 3-year period?

Table 5.1. Data from heather plants in (A) fenced and (B) unfenced areas of moor.

			A	B
1. Number of heather seedlings in a sample 1 m² plot:				
	September	1980	110	132
	April	1981	95	73
2. Total number of established heather plants (in 36m²):				
	August	1981	3648	1505
	August	1982	3417	1384
3. Mean height (mm) of plants:				
	September	1980	8.4	7.2
	April	1981	79.9	45.6
4. Dry weight (g) of 20 sample plants:				
	April	1981	9.4	2.5
5. Percentage cover of heather plants:				
	August	1982	26.7	6.2
	August	1983	42.5	21.5
6. Number of flowering stems of heather in a 0.1 m² quadrat:				
	October	1983	263	50
7. Number of capsules per stem:				
	November	1983	36.7	25.8

Problem 5.3   Exclosure experiments on rabbit grazing

Background When old grassland is cultivated, plants may regenerate either from seed or from regrowth of remaining vegetative fragments. However, the extent of regeneration, the type of plants which survive and the diversity of the community which results may all be affected by herbivory. The botanically diverse chalk grasslands of southern England are an example of an ecosystem which is maintained by grazing herbivores. The results given below are part of the total pool of results from an experiment designed to investigate the effects of grazing by rabbits on the early stages of plant recruitment.

Further reading

Crawley (1986: Ch. 4).

Data and questions The site was an acidic grassland with a long history of rabbit grazing. There were twelve plots in total in six pairs of plots forming blocks labelled A to F. All were

Table 5.2. Seedling densities (mean numbers per 0.25 m^2) of annual and short-lived perennial plants in fenced plots from each block (A–F). The species marked * are grasses. SE = standard error.

Species	A Mean	SE	B Mean	SE	C Mean	SE	D Mean	SE	E Mean	SE	F Mean	SE
Aira praecox	8.0	3.15	2.6	1.21	0	—	0	—	0	—	0	—
Aphanes microcarpa	4.2	1.88	0	—	0	—	0	—	0	—	3.6	1.08
Bromus hordeaceus	0	—	0	—	128.0	34.70	0	—	0	—	0	—
Capsella bursa-pastoris	0	—	0	—	2.4	1.03	0.2	0.20	39.0	8.70	2.0	0.32
Cerastium fontanum	0	—	0	—	6.0	1.70	2.0	0.95	3.8	0.97	0.6	0.40
Cerastium glomeratum	0	—	0	—	0	—	0	—	0	—	0.6	0.40
Crepis capillaris	0	—	0	—	4.0	1.30	5.6	1.21	5.4	1.89	27.2	5.01
Cytisis scoparius	0	—	0	—	0	—	0	—	35.0	4.37	0	—
Epilobium ciliatum	0	—	0	—	0	—	0	—	0.6	0.40	0.8	0.37
Fallopia convolvulus	0	—	0.4	0.40	0	—	0	—	0	—	0	—
Galium aparine	0	—	0	—	11.0	5.58	0.4	0.40	25.6	4.19	1.4	0.51
Lotus corniculatus	0.6	0.27	0.4	0.24	1.8	0.86	0.2	0.20	0.4	0.40	0.4	0.40
Medicago lupulina	0	—	0.2	0.20	0.4	0.24	4.6	1.40	4.8	1.59	1.4	0.51
Ornithopus perpusillus	2.2	0.37	1.4	0.51	0	—	0	—	0	—	0	—
Papaver dubium	0	—	0	—	7.8	3.68	5.4	1.60	47.2	18.95	2.8	0.80
Poa annua	0	—	0.2	0.20	0	—	0	—	0	—	0.8	0.49
Senecio sylvaticus	0	—	0	—	4.0	1.26	0	—	13.6	3.28	2.8	0.97
Silene latifolia alba	0	—	0	—	0.2	0.20	0	—	3.0	1.05	0	—
Spergularia arvensis	0	—	0.2	0.20	0	—	0.6	0.24	0	—	1.2	0.49
Tripleurospermum inodorum	0.4	0.24	0	—	0.6	0.40	0.4	0.24	9.8	2.87	3.2	0.80
Veronica persica	0	—	0	—	0	—	1.8	0.73	0	—	2.0	1.30
Vicia hirsuta	0	—	0	—	5.0	2.24	3.2	1.16	0	—	0	—
Vicia sativa	0.8	0.37	0	—	20.2	7.96	30.4	5.18	6.0	1.52	2.0	1.05
Total number	16.2	—	5.4	—	191.4	—	54.8	—	194.2	—	52.8	—
Number of species	6	—	7	—	13	—	12	—	13	—	16	—

Table 5.3. Shoot densities (means per 0.25 m²) from regrowth of perennial species in fenced plots from each block (A–F). The species marked ★ are grasses. SE = standard error.

Species	A Mean	A SE	B Mean	B SE	C Mean	C SE	D Mean	D SE	E Mean	E SE	F Mean	F SE
Achillea millefolium	1.6	0.93	1.6	0.68	2.2	0.86	0	—	3.4	1.50	2.2	1.07
Agrostis capillaris★	13.0	2.70	5.6	0.64	4.0	1.30	35.8	8.82	0	—	5.4	0.93
Anthoxanthemum odoratum★	48.4	8.23	58.6	6.38	0	—	39.2	3.68	0	—	74.6	9.29
Arrhenathum elatius★	0	—	0	—	10.0	2.30	2.0	1.05	0	—	0	—
Holcus lanatus★	0	—	0	—	0.6	0.40	20.2	3.28	9.8	2.03	20.8	2.71
Holcus mollis★	8.6	3.01	3.2	1.07	24.8	5.57	96.2	11.01	88.6	8.95	62.6	6.94
Luzula campestris	17.8	4.28	1.8	0.58	0	—	0	—	0	—	2.4	0.40
Plantago lanceolata	0	—	0	—	9.8	1.85	1.6	0.24	11.4	2.58	9.0	2.30
Rumex acetosa	0	—	0	—	5.2	2.56	16.2	3.23	0.4	0.24	10.2	2.48
Rumex acetosella	46.0	6.16	50.6	7.67	51.2	16.05	76.0	8.18	20.4	3.33	4.0	1.30
Senecio jacobaea	0	—	3.0	0.71	0	—	0	—	10.6	2.58	3.6	0.93
Stellaria graminea	2.6	0.68	1.6	0.51	142.2	22.55	83.0	8.37	94.4	8.21	183.4	12.15
Trifolium repens	0.6	0.40	0	—	3.2	0.80	18.8	5.19	1.6	0.68	2.0	0.89
Veronica chamaedrys	0	—	0	—	0.8	0.49	1.4	0.75	3.2	0.80	2.6	1.17
Total number	138.6	—	126.0	—	254.0	—	390.4	—	243.9	—	382.8	—
Number of species	8	—	8	—	11	—	11	—	10	—	13	—

cultivated by ploughing followed by rotovation, but after cultivation one plot from each pair was fenced to prevent rabbit grazing. Counts of numbers of seedlings and of shoots from regenerating vegetative fragments were made in five randomly placed 50 × 50 cm quadrats in each plot in April of the year following cultivation.

In both Tables 5.2 and 5.3 you should note the considerable variation between blocks in both seedling or shoot numbers and in species composition.

Similar data were recorded for seedlings and vegetative shoots in unfenced plots and the data in Tables 5.4 and 5.5 were then calculated.

Feel free to make any relevant comments that you may wish. The following questions may help you:

1. Which species are significantly more common and which less common when grazing is experienced?

2. What are the effects of rabbit grazing on the vegetation? Comment on any limitations in the data and briefly describe other data, either observational or experimental, that it would be useful to collect.

	Species	Degrees of freedom	Fenced mean	Grazed mean	SE of difference
Table 5.4. Mean seedling densities in fenced and unfenced plots. (The means are calculated over five replicate 50 × 50 cm quadrats only in those blocks where the species was present.) (SE = standard error.)	*Aira praecox*	1	5.3	6.2	1.88
	Aphanes microcarpa	1	3.9	0.4	0.47
	Bromus hordeaceu	0	128.0	15.2	6.81
	Capsella bursa-pastoris	3	10.9	2.2	1.07
	Cerastium fontanum	3	3.1	2.9	0.44
	Cerastium glomeratum	0	0.6	0.7	0.35
	Crepis capillaris	3	10.6	5.8	2.25
	Cytisis scoparius	0	35.0	5.1	4.92
	Epilobium ciliatum	1	0.7	0.8	0.57
	Fallopia convolvulus	0	0.4	0.6	0.57
	Galium aparine	3	9.6	2.3	3.11
	Lotus corniculatus	5	0.6	0.5	0.42
	Medicago lupulina	4	2.3	2.7	0.49
	Ornithopus perpusillus	1	1.8	1.2	0.64
	Papaver dubium	1	15.8	3.8	4.22
	Poa Annua	1	0.5	0.6	0.52
	Senecio sylvaticus	2	6.8	1.3	3.24
	Silene latifolia alba	1	1.6	0.9	0.87
	Spergula arvensis	2	0.7	1.1	0.38
	Tripleurospermum inodorum	4	2.9	2.3	1.13
	Veronica persica	1	1.9	2.2	0.67
	Vicia hirsuta	1	4.1	0.2	1.91
	Vicia sativa	4	11.9	3.9	3.53
	Total number		259.0	62.9	

	Species	Degrees of freedom	Fenced mean	Grazed mean	SE of difference
Table 5.5. Mean density of vegetative regrowth in fenced and unfenced plots. (The means are calculated over five replicate 50 × 50 cm quadrats only in those blocks where the species was present). (SE = standard error.)	*Achillea millefolium*	4	2.2	3.2	1.27
	Agrostis capillaris	4	12.8	23.1	7.13
	Anthoxanthum odoratum	3	55.2	75.8	13.38
	Arrhenatherum elatius	1	6.0	4.5	0.94
	Holcus lanatus	3	12.9	7.2	2.59
	Holcus mollis	5	47.3	27.3	12.72
	Luzula campestris	2	7.3	11.9	5.66
	Plantago lanceolata	3	7.9	10.2	3.11
	Rumex acetosa	3	8.0	3.5	2.64
	Rumex acetosella	5	41.4	64.1	12.02
	Senecio jacobaea	2	5.7	7.5	2.81
	Stellaria graminea	5	84.5	58.2	11.31
	Trifolium repens	4	5.2	3.3	0.98
	Veronica chamaedrys	3	2.0	2.4	0.39
	Total number		298.4	302.2	

Problem 5.4	Population of a sand martin colony

Background Man not only has effects directly on the land and the plants that colonise it, but indirectly affects the animals that live on it. Long-term changes in the diversity of animals or the population densities of particular species may therefore tell us about changes in habitats that may be more difficult to identify. Populations of animals are particularly hard to study because they are mobile, and particular individuals are often hard to identify. However, the example given below shows that investigations of population change are possible if the animals have a predictable home range and if they can be reliably marked.

Further reading

Krebs (1994), Begon (1979).

Data and questions The sand martin (*Riparia riparia*) is a small swallow-like holarctic bird whose Eurasian populations are trans-Saharan migrants, nesting colonially in holes in sandbanks, and feeding on small flying insects. Western European populations winter in the Sahel zone of Africa and arrive at the breeding colonies in March and April. They start to breed in their first year, and have two broods per year, averaging 4.78 eggs each. Survival from egg to chick is 0.88 and from chick to fledgeling (leaving the nest) is 0.78. First-year survival has been estimated to be 0.23, and adult annual survival has variously been estimated to be between 0.25 and 0.35. These figures have been derived from a variety of sources in western Europe.

So, using the above estimates of breeding success, and taking a hypothetical colony, stable at 100 pairs:

200 birds (100 pairs) lay two clutches of 4.78 eggs	= 956 eggs
0.88 of those eggs hatch	= 841 chicks
0.78 of those chicks fledge	= 656 juveniles
0.22 of those juveniles survive their first year	= 144 first year adults
0.28 of the old adults survive each year	= 56 old adults
144 first-year adults + 56 old adults	= 200 birds

The figure of 0.28 for adult survival has been taken from data for a particular English colony (Table 5.6) and the 0.22 for first-year survival has been calculated assuming a stable population, thus:

$$56 \text{ old adults} + 656 \times \text{juvenile survival} = 200$$

Therefore

$$S_j = (200\text{--}56)/656 = 0.22$$

Year	Population	Survival	Ingress
1968	—		
		0.1733	
1969	787		
		0.2953	1397
1970	1629		
		0.1705	745
1971	1023		
		0.2221	510
1972	737		
		0.1362	199
1973	299		
		0.4258	369
1974	496		
		0.5036	1076
1975	1326		
		0.3181	121
1976	542		
		0.3827	600
1977	808		
		0.2736	730
1978	951		
		0.3403	977
1979	1300		
		0.3013	436
1980	827		
		0.3033	567
1981	818		
		0.3438	513
1982	794		
		0.2632	491
1983	700		
		0.1518	60
1984	167		
		0.2866	122
1985	169		
		0.3796	195
1986	260		
		0.3137	176
1987	257		
		0.3025	275
1988	353		
		0.4266	491
1989	642		
		0.1942	181
1990	306		
1991	—	—	—
Mean	691	0.2800	487

Table 5.6. Mark–release–recapture estimates for the adult population of sand martins at a single colony. Survival and ingress are estimated between years; dashes represent incalculable estimates.

This estimate is very close to the 0.23 mentioned in the first paragraph.

A colony in central England has been studied for the last 24 years. One of the elements of the study has been the use of mark–release–recapture methods to estimate the population size, its annual survival rate and ingress (recruitment). Table 5.6 shows the estimates of these parameters.

So, in the hypothetical stable colony, 144 out of 200 adults are new recruits, i.e. 72 per cent. In the real colony (Table 5.6) 487 out of 691 adults are (on average) new recruits, i.e. 70.5 per cent. The number of new recruits per year required to bring the proportion up to 72 per cent is 498, i.e. 11 more.

1. Plot the three sets of data in Table 5.6 on a *single* graph with year on the x-axis; use bars or lines as you wish. Label your graph appropriately.

2. Comment on the problems involved in mixing data from various sources and of real or theoretical origin. Does this produce an unacceptable circularity in the data here presented?

3. You have not been informed of the standard errors of the estimates. What use would you make of them if you had been so informed? In which ways might they influence your interpretation of the data?

Note: In all subsequent questions assume that the mark–release–recapture estimates represent the true population parameters (i.e. ignore the possible influence of standard errors).

4. How relevant are average figures when there are such large annual fluctuations?

5. Do the figures in Table 5.6 indicate that variations in the adult population size are a consequence of variations in ingress, survival or both?

6. On the basis of the data presented in Table 5.6, is it possible to say whether variations in ingress are due to variations in the nest success of the previous year, or to variations in first-year survival, or to immigration from other colonies?

7. If you were responsible for managing the colony and the surrounding land, what further information would you require in order to assess the importance of the apparent shortfall of eleven recruits?

8. Do you think that the colony is self-sustaining in the long term? Give reasons for your opinion.

Problem 5.5 — Decline and overfishing of a cod fishery

Background

Harvesting of fish stocks can greatly affect the population dynamics of the fish. With the removal of large numbers of adults, fewer young may be produced each year and population numbers may oscillate and fall disastrously. The destruction of the Newfoundland fishery is one catastrophic example. Around Europe, quotas on catches have been introduced to protect the falling fish stocks. It is hoped that understanding the ways in which fishing affects the size and stability of fish populations may help us devise strategies for their sustained exploitation.

Further reading

Begon *et al.* (1986: Ch. 10), Begon and Mortimer (1981: Ch. 5).

Data and questions

Figure 5.4 and Table 5.7 give information on the status of the north-east arctic stock of cod (*Gadus morhua*) during the period 1946–80. Prior to 1977, there was an international agreement that the total allowable catch should be set at 0.75×10^6 t year^{-1}. From 1977 onwards this was reduced to 0.3×10^6 tonne year^{-1}.

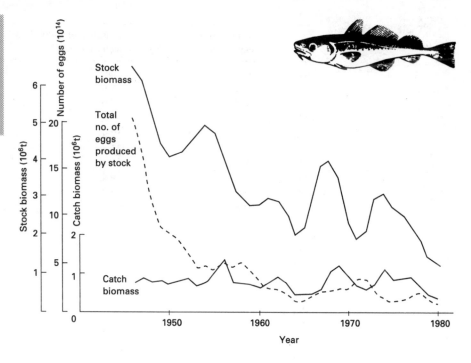

Figure 5.4. The levels of stock biomass, numbers of eggs produced and the catch biomass of north-east Arctic cod during the period 1946–80.

1. Describe the main trends in the stock biomass, egg production and catch during the period 1946–80.

2. Interpret the main trends in the stock biomass and egg production in the light of the data on the catch. Discuss the difficulties in using data of this kind to determine the effect of exploitation on the stock.

3. Investigate and comment on the relationship between total number of eggs produced each year and the number of individuals aged 1 year surviving 1 year later.

4. What advice would you give for the management of the stock during the 1980s? Make sure that you justify your suggestions.

Year	Total number of eggs produced/(10^{14})	Number of individuals aged 1 year/(10^6)
1946	20.5	—
1947	16.9	7.0
1948	11.8	10.6
1949	8.9	16.2
1950	8.0	17.8
1951	7.4	23.8
1952	6.0	16.6
1953	4.6	10.4
1954	4.7	6.6
1955	4.4	12.0
1956	5.0	7.5
1957	4.7	10.3
1958	5.1	11.8
1959	4.4	13.8
1960	3.1	10.9
1961	2.6	7.1
1962	2.4	5.1
1963	1.9	11.6
1964	1.2	7.7
1965	1.1	11.1
1966	1.7	2.5
1967	2.3	1.7
1968	2.2	2.9
1969	2.4	6.0
1970	2.4	15.2
1971	3.4	8.3
1972	3.4	7.8
1973	2.0	9.3
1974	1.2	9.2
1975	1.1	5.2
1976	1.2	9.8
1977	1.6	3.2
1978	2.0	2.2
1979	1.2	2.5
1980	0.8	2.0

Table 5.7. Data on north-east arctic cod.

SOLUTIONS

Problem 5.1

1. To determine the discharge it is necessary to know both the average velocity of the river and its cross-sectional area. The former can be measured using propeller flow meters submerged at various points or by measuring the velocity of objects floating just below the surface of the stream: the latter by surveying the contours of the river bed.

2. See Fig. 5.5. At a river height of 4 m the loss of sediment is around 112 kg s^{-1}.

3. The rate of discharge of sediment at 2-hourly intervals can be read off the discharge/height graph (Fig. 5.5) and is given in Table 5.8.

    It can be assumed without much loss of accuracy that each rate of discharge is continued for the subsequent 2-hour period. The total discharge of each 2-hour period can be found, therefore, by multiplying the discharge rate by the length of time = 2 × 60 × 60 s = 7200 secs.

    $$\text{Total discharge} = 2275 \times 7200 = 1.64 \times 10^7 \text{ kg}$$

4. The depth of soil which is eroded is the volume of sediment divided by the area over which it was spread.

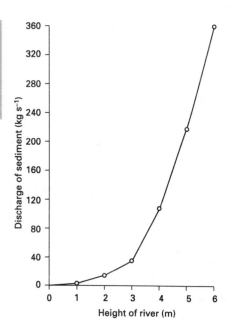

Figure 5.5. The relationship between the height of the Segama river and its rate of discharge of sediment.

Time (hours)	Discharge (kg s^{-1})
0	16
2	36
4	112
6	220
8	360
10	360
12	360
14	286
16	220
18	162
20	112
22	70
24	36
26	25
Cumulative	2275

Table 5.8. Discharge of the river Segama following the storm.

$$\text{Volume of soil} = \text{Mass/density}$$

$$= 1.64 \times 10^7/1.4 \times 10^3$$

$$= 1.17 \times 10^4 \text{ m}^3$$

$$= 1.2 \times 10^4 \text{ m}^3 \text{ to two significant figures}$$

$$\text{Area of catchment} = 3000 \text{ km}^2$$

$$= 3.000 \times 10^9 \text{ m}^2$$

$$\text{Depth of soil eroded} = 1.17 \times 10^4/3 \times 10^9 \text{ m}^2$$

$$= 4.0 \times 10^{-6} \text{ m}$$

The average depth of soil eroded is around 4 μm, which is very small. Even if 25 storms occur in a year the total loss of soil will be only one-tenth of a millimetre!

5. High sediment concentrations may have harmful effects on water plants growing in the river by both physically covering them and reducing light levels. Loss of plants might subsequently result in a reduction in the numbers and diversity of aquatic invertebrates and fish. These effects must be investigated by determining the diversity in streams flowing from logged and unlogged areas.

6. The depth of soil eroded is

$$90/(20 \times 2 \times 1400) \text{ m}$$

$$= 1.6 \times 10^{-3} \text{ m}$$

$$= 1.6 \text{ mm}$$

The value calculated from these field experiments is some 400 times that calculated using the river data. There are two main reasons for this. First, despite heavy logging, only a small fraction of the ground will have been bare. Tropical vegetation recovers rapidly from damage and soon after logging bare ground is covered up by a luxurious growth of vines. Second, tests on the sediment concentration in the river only measure the amount of soil that was washed into the river. Much soil might have eroded but moved down slopes only a short distance, and much soil may have been trapped in areas of vegetation before it reached the river. Belts of vegetation next to rivers are commonly left after logging for just this purpose.

Problem 5.2

1. The first count of heather seedlings in September 1980 is a measure of the germination success of the plants in the two areas. This is higher in plot B, possibly because of fertilisation by sheep droppings. The second count in April 1981 records those plants which have survived the first year. Combined with the first count, this gives a measure for the survivorship of seedlings over their first winter. Grazing seems to reduce survivorship because it is much higher (86 per cent) for seedlings in the protected plot, A, than for the unfenced area, B (55 per cent).

2. These data show that the numbers of established plants after 1.5 and 2.5 years are much greater in the ungrazed plot, A, than in the grazed plot, B. These results can be combined with those from 1 to give values for percentage survivorship.

Survivorship after	A (%)	B (%)
1.5 years	92	32
2.5 years	86	29

3. These data show that the shoot lengths are lower in plot B, particularly after a year. This is probably because they have been grazed by the sheep.

4. Year-old plants in B also have a much lower biomass than those in A, again due to grazing.

    Data from lines 1 and 4 can be combined to calculate the standing biomass of heather after 1 year in April 1981:

    $$\text{Dry mass in A} = 95 \times 9.4/20 = 44.6 \text{ g m}^{-2}$$

    $$\text{Dry mass in B} = 73 \times 2.5/20 = 9.1 \text{ g m}^{-2}$$

    Hence the biomass in B is less than a quarter of that in A after 1 year.

5. These data show that in both plots the amount of cover increases with time: heather is gradually covering the ground. However, the grazing in B slows the spread of the heather, allowing more bare ground to be exposed.

6–7. Data from lines 6 and 7 show that after 3 years the reproductive capacity of the heather is greatly reduced by grazing, since there are fewer flowering heads, each of which produces fewer seed capsules. The total number of capsules produced per $0.1\ m^2$ quadrat can be calculated by multiplying the number of flower heads by the number of capsules in each stem.

Capsules produced in A $= 263 \times 36.7 = 9650$ per quadrat

Capsules produced in B $= 50 \times 25.8 = 1290$ per quadrat.

Therefore grazing has reduced the reproductive capacity of the heather after 3 years to only one-seventh of that in the ungrazed plot.

Problem 5.3

1. Because of the considerable variation between the blocks there are very few species for which the data provide reliable evidence of the effect of grazing. Significant differences in shoot densities only occur where the difference between the means exceeds a certain multiple of the standard error of the difference, depending on the number of degrees of freedom. For significant differences at the 5 per cent level the multiple is 12.7, 4.3, 3.2, 2.8 and 2.6 for 1 to 5 degrees of freedom. Of the seedlings, only *Capsella bursa-pastoris* is significantly more common in the fenced areas. *Bromus hordaceous* and *Cytisus scoparius* also appear to be more common, but it is impossible to tell whether there are significant differences because there are data from only one block, and there are no degrees of freedom. None of the regrowing perennials show significant differences in density between the areas.

2. In general it seems that grazing reduces the number of seedlings, but has no effect on the number of regenerating shoots. However, with the data given it is impossible to test this statistically because only the mean total densities are given. It would be necessary to go back to the original data to obtain values for the numbers of seedlings and regenerating shoots in each plot in fenced and unfenced areas. These data could then be analysed statistically like those for the single species.

   If rabbit grazing does reduce the numbers of annual species regenerating, it will hasten the domination of perennial species, a process which generally occurs anyway during plant succession following disturbance. Rabbits probably destroy more seedlings than regenerating shoots because they are easier to uproot and because annuals are less likely than perennials to possess efficient chemical or mechanical defences against herbivory.

   However, the data presented do not give any real indication of the effect of grazing on the *amount* of vegetation, which might well be reduced. It would be a good idea to measure percentage cover or the biomass of vegetation. Grazing might also reduce the reproductive potential of those plants which do survive. It would be useful to compare the number of flowerheads in the grazed and ungrazed area.

Problem 5.4

1. To produce a comprehensible graph it is best to plot the total population for each year and then to split this total into the ingress and the surviving adults. (This

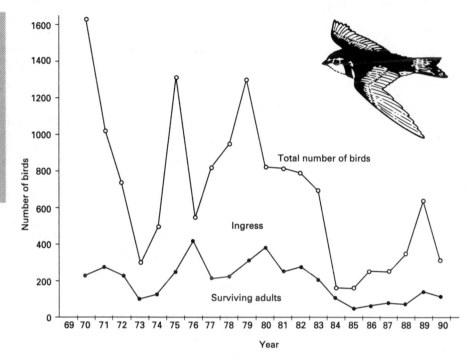

Figure 5.6. Graph showing the adult population of a sand martin colony (○) in the years from 1970 to 1990. Numbers of adults surviving from the previous year is shown at the bottom of the graph (●), while the ingress of unmarked individuals is the area between the two lines.

equals the total for the year minus the ingress from the previous year. It also equals the previous year's population multiplied by the survivorship.) The resulting graph is shown in Fig. 5.6. This allows one to investigate the composition of the population each year at a glance and to investigate population fluctuations.

2. It is very dangerous to mix data from different sources. It is all too easy to use theoretical data to generate data which can then be used to prove the theory! Provided the mean survival values are used with care, however, they can be extremely useful, as they can be used to determine whether the birds were relatively more or less successful in a particular year.

3. Standard error bars would have been added to Fig. 5.6. These would have helped to show whether the fluctuations in the population estimates were due to real fluctuations in the population or were merely due to the errors inherent in the technique.

4. Average figures are hardly relevant when annual fluctuations are so high. In particular it is dangerous to use mean values of survivorship to calculate the long-term changes in population. For instance, if there are 100 adults with survivorship of 100 per cent after 1 year and 0 per cent after the second, the population after 2 years will be 0. However, the *mean* survivorship will be 50 per cent, so calculations based on this figure will suggest a population of 25 after 2 years.

5. It can be seen from Fig. 5.6 that variations in the population size are largely a consequence of variations in ingress; the numbers of returning adults is lower and, in general, more constant.

6. It is not possible to say what influences the variations in ingress. Undoubtedly all three factors: nest success, first-year survival and immigration may be important but since the origin of incoming birds cannot be identified, exactly which is unclear.

7. To assess the importance of the apparent shortfall, I would require information on how the habitat around the colony has changed in the last 20 years. I would also need information about the changes in other colonies near by.

8. There seems to be evidence of a long-term decline in the colony, especially after the early 1980s when both the numbers of surviving adults and the ingress seem to fall.

Problem 5.5 1. The general trend from 1946 to 1980 is of decline in both the stock biomass and egg production. However, superimposed on this decline are large cyclic fluctuations in the stock biomass which have a period of about 6–7 years. Catch biomass has remained fairly stable over the whole period, though it may have started to decline over the last few years when quotas were reduced. The catch biomass also shows some evidence of cyclic fluctuations of the same period as those of the stock biomass, but which tend to lag a year or two behind those of the stock biomass.

2. The exploitation of the cod may well have been responsible both for the decline in the population and for the population cycling.

   The mean level of the catch biomass is relatively high compared with the stock (indeed it often exceeds the quota), so catching fish might well be reducing the population faster than it can be replaced. The fact that there is a yearly quota for the catch might also be causing the stock to decline; when the population is low, more effort will be put into fishing to endeavour to maximise the amount of fish caught (and so not lose out). This would further reduce the population and may be driving the stock to extinction. However, a decline in the habitat might also be partly responsible for the long-term decline in stocks.

   Since more fish are caught when the stock biomass is high than when it is low, harvesting the fish might also cause the population to cycle. However, it is difficult to say whether or not fishing is the cause of this trend. The cycling might also be a natural phenomenon, caused by a reduction in survival of young fish when the adult population is high. Some evidence for this can be identified from Table 5.7; the number of year old individuals seems to show similar cycles, peaking when the adult population is low and being low when the adult population is high.

   It is difficult to determine the effect of fishing since we cannot compare the stocks with that of an unexploited control population.

3. The relationship between the yearly egg production and the number which survive to the next year is shown in Fig. 5.7 which seems to describe a parabola, rising to a peak at an egg production of around 8×10^{14} and falling above this value. This recruitment curve is typical of a population which is limited by intraspecific competition. In years in which there are low levels of egg production,

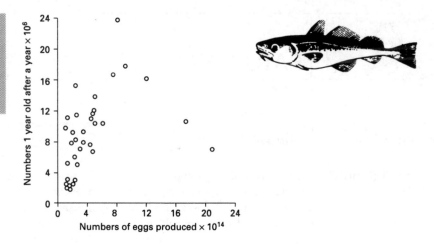

Figure 5.7. The relationship between the number of eggs produced in a year and the number of young surviving after 1 year.

the number of fish surviving is more or less proportional to the number of eggs because the *chances* of survival are unaffected. At high levels of egg production, however, there is strong intraspecific competition between the young fish. As a result large numbers die and the actual number surviving falls.

4. During the 1980s it will clearly not be possible to sustain a quota of 0.3×10^6 t year^{-1}; its use will drive the population of cod even lower. Other strategies are much better for the survival of the cod, if not for the short-term economics of the fishermen. One is to allow only a constant fishing *effort*, perhaps by limiting the number, size and operating time of trawlers. The other is to allow the removal only of a fixed percentage of the population. These should both prevent the population from being decimated during a poor year, since then only few fish will be taken. Both, however, would be difficult to implement and unpopular, as there will not be a stable supply of fish and both trawlermen and fishing ports will be hard hit during bad years.

6 FARMING

Nitrate leaching

Background
In recent years the concentration of nitrate in rivers draining arable areas has increased remarkably. This is a problem because high levels of nitrate promote the growth of blooms of algae which can shade out larger plants and use up the available oxygen, killing fish and other animals. Blooms of blue–green algae can also produce toxins which are lethal both to man and to livestock. For this reason the EU has set a limit of 11.3 mg N l^{-1} for water supplies.

There is seldom a problem of nitrate leaching on ground covered by natural vegetation or by permanent pasture because the living plants reincorporate nitrates released by dead material. The situation in arable farming, however, is rather different because much of the nitrogen (N) is removed when the crop is harvested, and this must be replaced each year. In temperate regions, agricultural practice may also leave the soil bare for some months of the year. As a result, the microbial activity which has been stimulated by cultivation will produce nitrates when there is no crop to use them, and leaching can occur. To prevent this the winter ground is nowadays often covered by a catch crop such as mustard which incorporates these nitrates and can be ploughed in just before sowing of the next crop in the spring to help fertilise it. Even so, the spring crop's demand for N must be met by extra N fertiliser. This is converted by microbes to nitrates, and as well as going into the crop, some is incorporated into soil organic matter, some is denitrified to dinitrogen or nitrous oxide gases, and some is washed from the soil, contributing to the nitrate problem.

Further reading

Addiscott *et al.* (1991), Briggs and Courtney (1989: Ch. 4).

Data and questions
Table 6.1 shows the relationship between the amount of nitrogen applied to a crop of winter wheat and the amount of nitrogen in the soil after the crop is harvested.

1. Plot the relationship on a graph, and from the graph estimate (a) how much nitrogen is already available in soil, and (b) the optimal amount of nitrogen which should be applied to maximise profits while minimising leaching.

Grassland, for grazing or cut for silage, has a longer growing period than cereals, and 400 kg N ha^{-1} can be applied before leaching of nitrate occurs. However, if grassland is grazed at average stock density (e.g. three cattle per hectare) then most of the

kg N ha^{-1} applied to crop	kg N ha^{-1} in soil post-harvest
0	51
80	60
120	60
160	54
200	70
240	93
280	110

Table 6.1. The relationship between the amount of nitrogen applied to a crop of winter wheat and the amount of nitrogen in the soil after the crop is harvested.

nitrogen incorporated into grass and eaten is returned in urine or faeces. This return of nitrogen is in such concentrated patches that it cannot be captured and recycled by the microbes–grass system and thus 300 of the 400 kg N ha^{-1} applied will leach away.

2. What amount of throughflow of water is required to reduce this leaching below the EU limit?

Table 6.2 shows the fluctuating levels of nitrate in the river Thames each month.

3. Comment on the data in Table 6.2, in terms of spring applications of fertiliser, and rainfall driving the leaching.

The effect of ploughing up permanent pasture is to release about 4 t N ha^{-1} over a period of 20–25 years.

4. From the data in Table 6.3, comment on the contribution of this practice to the nitrate problem.

Table 6.2. Monthly amounts of nitrate (as 1000s of tonnes of nitrogen) in the river Thames, together with average daily amounts of evaporation and rainfall (in mm).

	Nitrogen in river	Evaporation	Rainfall
January	22	0.3	2.1
February	26	0.4	1.5
March	27	0.9	2.0
April	18	1.9	1.5
May	12	2.7	1.7
June	9	3.3	1.9
July	7	3.4	1.5
August	6	3.4	1.4
September	7	2.3	1.7
October	8	1.2	1.9
November	12	0.5	2.4
December	21	0.3	2.2

Table 6.3. Areas of land in Cambridgeshire growing grass or cereal.

Year	Cereals (%)	Grass (%)
1942	66	24
1952	70	22
1962	70	20
1972	80	12
1982	85	8

Problem 6.2   Economics of nitrogen and water supply to crops

Background

Farming is based on a practical knowledge of biology, but farmers are essentially businessmen whose aim is to make a maximum sustainable profit from their land. Modern farming relies heavily on the use of man-made fertilisers to supply those elements to plants which would otherwise limit growth. Nitrogen, phosphorus and potassium are the elements which most commonly limit growth and which are most often applied. The application of water, either by spraying or by irrigation, is also important, particularly at low latitudes where drought can be a major problem. The farmer must weigh up the costs of the different treatments and calculate which, on average, will bring the best returns.

Further reading

Addiscott *et al.* (1991), Briggs and Courtney (1989: Ch. 4).

Data and questions

A local agricultural research programme has been established to determine the economics of growing a new crop, millet, in a North African country. The country is largely farmed by owner-occupiers and there is little scope for increasing the area of land under cultivation in the country. Experiments have been carried out on an agricultural research station to assess the response of the crop to applied nitrogen-based fertiliser (Table 6.4) and to irrigation (Table 6.5).

Using the information provided in the tables and under 'extra information', and your biological knowledge, answer the following questions:

1. Draw a table showing the relationship between the amount of fertiliser applied and the profit per hectare in the absence of irrigation. (Profit is the amount of money the farmer has left after selling the crop and after paying all expenses.)

2. How much fertiliser would you recommend the average farmer to apply and on what grounds would you make that recommendation?

Table 6.4. Relationship between the amount of fertiliser applied and yield of millet.	Fertiliser (kg ha^{-1})	Yield (t ha^{-1})
	0	0.6
	40	1.0
	60	1.3
	80	1.4
	100	1.45

Fertiliser experiment

The millet crop was sown in a well prepared seed bed on 3 March 1985. The field used for the experiment had been used to grow wheat in 1983 and had been left fallow in 1984. The experimental plots were replicated five times and the average results are presented in Table 6.4. The fertiliser was applied at the time of sowing in bands just beneath the drills. No irrigation was provided. The crop was harvested on 5 September 1985. The yield of seed was measured and corrected to give equivalent % moisture where necessary.

Table 6.5. Relationship between the depth of irrigation water applied and the yield of millet.	Water (mm)	Yield (t ha^{-1})
	0	1.0
	20	1.1
	40	1.4
	60	1.65
	80	1.65
	100	1.65

Irrigation experiment

The crop was sown, grown and harvested as described above, in a field adjacent to that used for the fertiliser experiment. The field had been allowed to lie fallow in 1983 and had been used to grow field beans (a leguminous crop) in 1984. The irrigation was provided by simple flooding from irrigation channels running through the fields On each occasion when irrigation was given, 10 mm of water was provided (i.e. equivalent to the field being given sufficient water such that a layer of water 10 mm deep would have formed had the water not run into the soil). The irrigation treatment was begun in mid May and repeated at weekly intervals for some plots. A plot receiving a total of 10 mm water would have received water on the first occasion only, while those plots receiving 20 mm were watered on two successive weeks and so on; thus plots receiving 100 mm water were watered each week for 10 weeks.

3. How many cubic metres of water must be applied per hectare to provide 10 mm of water?

4. Using the information provided, calculate how much water should be added to the millet crop to maximise the profit to the farmer.

5. Comment on the relationship between the amount of water added to the crop and the yield. Suggest some reasons why adding more than 60 mm of water over the season does not appear to increase the yield. Very briefly outline how you would investigate these possibilities and how you might improve the design of the irrigation experiment.

6. In the irrigation experiment (Table 6.5) no nitrogen was added to the crop. Despite this the control unirrigated plots produced a higher yield than similar plots in the fertiliser experiment (Table 6.4). Offer a possible explanation.

Extra information

Cost of cultivating field, buying seed, sowing and weeding was 20 AU ha^{-1}. (The AU is the local currency.) Cost of harvesting crop = 2 AU ha^{-1} + 1 AU t^{-1}; average value of millet = 60 AU t^{-1}; cost of fertiliser = 0.5 AU kg^{-1}; cost of irrigation water = 0.03 AU m^{-3}.

In answering this question you can assume that all the experimental plots were sufficiently uniform that statistical considerations need not apply.

Problem 6.3 | **Effect of seeding rate on performance of winter wheat**

Background

Lodging of cereal crops, in which the plants fall over, has long been a problem in world agriculture. Wheat, barley, maize and rice all lodge and it is a major factor limiting production; addition of high levels of nitrogen greatly increases the chances of lodging, resulting in ears which have reduced yield and quality and which are more difficult to harvest. Much effort has been put into the prevention of lodging by agronomists and plant breeders and modern cultivars are both shorter and stiffer-stemmed than earlier ones. However, because of their heavier heads, lodging still occurs.

Further reading

Briggs and Courtney (1989: Chs. 3 and 8), Easson *et al.* (1993).

Data and questions

This problem relates to field trials, which were carried out in Northern Ireland over the years 1989–90, to determine how altering the density of seed application affected the development, resistance to lodging and grain yield of winter wheat *Triticum aestivum*. The results of the trials are summarised in Tables 6.6 and 6.7 and in Fig. 6.1.

1. How does the rate of seeding affect the growth and morphology of plants?

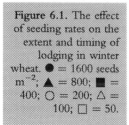

Table 6.6. The morphological characteristics of wheat crops sown at seeding densities from 50 to 1600 m^{-2}. Results were obtained from the destructive sampling of twelve 0.25 m^2 quadrats on 24 July 1990 at grain filling.

	Seed rate (m^{-2})						
	50	100	200	400	800	1600	SE
Straw yield (kg Ha^{-1})	4290	4434	4112	3849	3213	3292	242
Plants (m^{-2})	41.7	80.6	151.2	260.2	391.5	640.4	10.6
Stems (m^{-2})	317	375	449	505	568	858	20.6
Ears (m^{-2})	253	326	389	481	635	855	16.7
Grain weight (mg)	53.5	54.0	52.8	47.8	44.7	42.7	0.92
Grains/ear	55.9	53.1	47.9	33.3	23.1	15.3	1.57
Crop height (cm)	84.5	86.5	88.9	89.3	86.9	84.8	0.66

Table 6.7. Grain yield of wheat obtained by traditional harvesting of the crop on 18 August when the crop was fully ripe.

Seed rate (m^{-2})	50	100	200	400	800	1600
Yield (t ha^{-1})	9.51	9.65	7.81	5.63	4.19	2.79

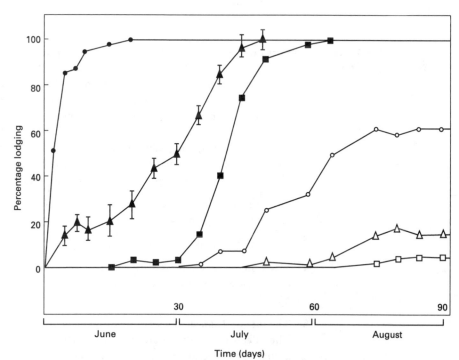

Figure 6.1. The effect of seeding rates on the extent and timing of lodging in winter wheat. ● = 1600 seeds m^{-2}; ▲ = 800; ■ = 400; ○ = 200; △ = 100; □ = 50.

2. How does seed rate affect the susceptibility of wheat to lodging? Use the information provided to suggest why this is the case.

3. For each seeding rate, calculate the mass of grain per hectare on wheat plants on 24 July. How do these differ from the amounts harvested on 14 August and why?

4. Farmers usually sow wheat at a rate of around 400 seeds m^{-2}. Why do you think they sow at this rate rather than the optimal rate of 100 seeds m^{-2}?

Problem 6.4   Integrated pest management

Background   The use of chemical pesticides has revolutionised farming methods and greatly contributed to the increases in crop yields which have been achieved since the Second World War. However, this has been achieved at great environmental cost: invertebrate diversity has been greatly reduced in industrialised countries, and the demise of butterflies has been particularly notable. Pesticides may also kill the predators and parasites of pest species which might act as a biological control. In some cases, therefore, the use of pesticides can make outbreaks of pests potentially *more* damaging. We clearly need to be more aware of what we are doing to organisms other than the target species, and try to develop more selective pesticides.

Further reading

Briggs and Courtney (1989: Ch. 6), Burn *et al.* (1987).

Data and questions   The larva of the ladybird beetle *Coccinella fransiscana* is predatory on the spotted alfalfa aphid *Therioaphis trifolii*, a serious pest of lucerne in California. *C. fransiscana*, and other predators and parasitoids, are used in the biological control of *T. trifolii*. The lucerne variety 'Lahontan' is markedly resistant to attack by *T. trifolii*; *T. trifolii* can also be controlled by insecticides, such as malathion.

1. Plot the percentage mortality of *Therioaphis*, fed on lucerne treated with various concentrations of the insecticide malathion, from the data in Table 6.8, using a photocopy of the log × probit graph paper provided (Fig.6.2).

2. Plot, similarly, the percentage mortality of *C. fransiscana* exposed to similar concentrations (Table 6.8).

3. State the LC$_{50}$s of the herbivore and the predator.

4. Many herbivores possess very effective oxidative enzymes to metabolise plant toxins. How could this relate to the difference in response of *C. fransiscana* and *T. trifolii*?

5. The diet of *T. trifolii* in a second test is changed to the resistant 'Lahontan' variety. The effects of malathion are shown in Table 6.9. Plot the percentage mortality against log concentration, and state the LC$_{50}$.

Table 6.8. Relationship between the concentration of malathion applied and the mortality of *T. trifolii* and *C. fransiscana*.	Concentration of malathion (mg l^{-1})	% mortality of *T. trifolii*	% mortality of *C. fransiscana*
	0	2	2
	5	12	4
	10	26	50
	30	74	97
	50	82	99
	100	94	99

Table 6.9. Relationship between the concentration of malathion applied and the mortality of *T. trifolii* fed on the lucerne variety 'Lahotan'.	Concentration of malathion (mg l^{-1})	% mortality of *T. trifolii*
	0	10
	5	22
	10	62
	30	89
	50	95
	100	99

Table 6.10. Relationship between the concentration of pirimicarb applied and the mortality of *T. trifolii* and *C. fransiscana*.	Concentration of pirimicarb (mg l^{-1})	% mortality of *T. trifolii*	% mortality of *C. fransiscana*
	0	2	3
	5	2	2
	10	4	1
	30	30	6
	50	58	22
	100	85	48

6. Briefly discuss the potential of the resistant cultivar as part of an integrated pest management (IPM) strategy.

7. Plot the percentage mortality of herbivore and predator to pirimicarb (Table 6.10). State, with reasons, whether pirimicarb or malathion would be more effective in an IPM programme to control spotted alfalfa aphid.

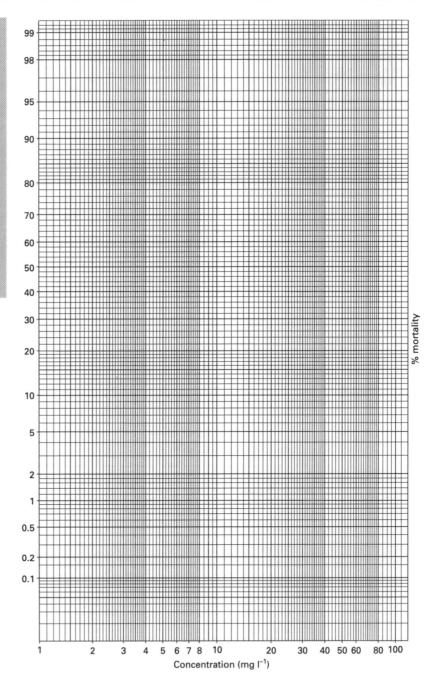

Figure 6.2. Log × probit paper. The concentration of the applied chemical is put on to logged x-axis (here $\log_{10}$). Percentage mortality, meanwhile, should be plotted up the y-axis, which is contracted near the middle. These axes usually result in a straight line of % mortality vs log concentration. The LC_{50} is found by determining where this line crosses 50% mortality.

SOLUTIONS

Problem 6.1   1. (a)   Figure 6.3 shows that between 50 and 60 kg N ha^{-1} is always present in soil after harvest, even if very small amounts of nitrogen are added.

   (b)   Figure 6.3 shows a sudden change of slope at an application rate of nitrogen of 160 kg ha^{-1}. Above this value more nitrate is left in the soil after harvest. Therefore there are two disadvantages of applying more than this amount: first, there is likely to be leaching of this extra nitrate over the winter; second, much of the the extra nitrate applied by the farmer will not be taken up by the plant and so will be wasted; 160 kg ha^{-1} is therefore likely to be the optimum rate to apply.

2.   Throughflow of water comes from rainfall. 1 ha is 100 × 100 m, i.e. 10 000 m^2. Therefore 1 cm of rain over 1 ha represents a volume of 100 m^3 or 100 000 l.

   The EU limit is stated above to be 11.3 mg N l^{-1}, i.e. 11.3 mg N in 1 l of water. This is equivalent to 1.13 × 10^{-2} kg in 1 m^3. Thus to clear 300 kg N from a hectare would require 300/1.13 × 10^{-2} = 2.65 × 10^4 m^3 of water. Spread over 1 ha (10^4 m^2) this would come to a depth of 2.65 m, or 265 cm. (265 cm of rain – over 100 inches – is about three times the average rainfall! But what proportion of fields are grazed, and what proportion of grazed fields are receiving that amount of input as fertiliser?)

3.   The amounts of nitrogen in river water peak in winter and are lowest in summer. (Data are presented as amounts of nitrogen, not as concentration, so no adjustment need be made for seasonal differences in volume of water in the river.) This does not match the timing of nitrogen fertiliser applications. The leaching does not

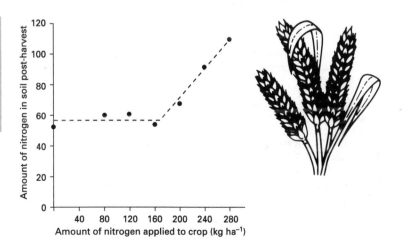

Figure 6.3. The relationship between the amount of nitrogen applied to a crop and the amount which remains in the soil post-harvest.

initially relate to rainfall, until evaporation rates are subtracted from rainfall – only rain which does not evaporate can carry the nitrate through the soil.

4. Table 6.3 shows that the extent of arable land has increased by 19 per cent of the total and grassland decreased by 16 per cent of the total over several decades. The ploughing of grasslands would result in an increase in nitrate leaching.

Over a 20-year period the release of nitrogen would be 4 t ha^{-1} of grassland lost. Therefore the average amount of nitrogen lost per year equals $4/20 = 2 \times 10^{-1}$ t ha^{-1} year$^{-1} = 200$ kg ha^{-1} year^{-1}. This is only slightly lower than the amount of leaching that would occur if all the grassland was heavily fertilised and grazed (300 kg ha^{-1} year^{-1}). Therefore ploughing up the land will be a heavy contributor to nitrate leaching. This may be the real reason for the increased levels of nitrate we now detect in our water and will have a bigger contribution than that due to leaching from long-established arable land.

Problem 6.2

1. The profit per hectare equals the value of the crop (yield × value per tonne) minus the combined costs of cultivation, harvest and fertiliser. It is best to tabulate the data (Table 6.11).

2. I would recommend the average farmer to apply 60 kg ha^{-1}, the level at which profit is maximised. Above this point extra application of fertiliser does not improve yield enough to pay for itself.

3. Spread over 1 ha, 10 mm of water has dimensions $100 \times 100 \times 0.01$ m. The volume is therefore $100 \times 100 \times 0.01 = 100$ m^3.

4. Again the profit per hectare equals the value of the crop (yield × value per tonne) minus the combined costs of cultivation, harvest and water. It is best to draw out a table (Table 6.12). From this we can see that to maximise the profit it would be best to apply 60 mm water.

5. Adding small quantities of water to the crop was ineffective in increasing the yield, possibly because it may have been added before the main period of growth occurred when water was the limiting factor. This may also have been the reason why adding more than 60 mm was ineffective – it was added *after* the major growth spurt. To investigate these possibilities one would irrigate different plots at different times, measuring both growth and yield concurrently.

Table 6.11. Relationship between the rate of fertiliser applied, the crop yield and value, the cost of cultivation, harvest and fertiliser and the net profit.

Fertiliser rate (kg ha^{-1})	Yield (t ha^{-1})	Value (AU)	Costs (AU)			Profit (AU)
			Cultivation	Harvest	Fertiliser	
0	0.6	36	20	2.6	0	13.4
40	1.0	60	20	3.0	20	17.0
60	1.3	78	20	3.3	30	24.7
80	1.4	84	20	3.4	40	20.6
100	1.45	87	20	3.45	50	13.55

Table 6.12. Relationship between the depth of water applied, the yield and value of the crop, the costs of cultivation, harvest and water and hence the net profit.	Water (mm)	Yield (t ha^{-1})	Value (AU)	Costs (AU)			Profit (AU)
				Cultivation	Harvest	Water	
	0	1.0	60	20	3.0	0	37.0
	20	1.1	66	20	3.1	6	36.9
	40	1.4	84	20	3.4	12	48.6
	60	1.65	99	20	3.65	18	57.35
	80	1.65	99	20	3.65	24	51.35
	100	1.65	99	20	3.65	30	45.35

The problem with the design of the irrigation experiment is that two factors, amount of water and timing of irrigation, are mixed up. To investigate the effect of altering the amount of water added, it would be better to add water for the same length of time to each plot, but varying the amount added. Plots would therefore receive either 2, 4, 6, 8 or 10 mm of water each week.

6. The control in the irrigation experiment had a higher yield than that of the first experiment because it was planted on land that had had its nitrogen levels increased by being planted with a nitrogen-fixing crop, field beans, the year before. Nitrogen levels would have been reduced in the other field by growing wheat in it the year before.

Problem 6.3

1. Plants grown at lower seed rates are no taller than ones grown at high rates but each plant has a greater number of stems, each of which, having a higher mass, is probably thicker. Each of these stems, in turn holds up a larger number of slightly heavier grains.

2. Wheat sown at higher rates lodges earlier and more extensively than that sown at low seed rates. This may be related to differences in straw morphology. Plants sown at the higher rate have thinner, probably weaker stems and for this reason may fall over more easily.

3. The mass of grain can be calculated using the data in Table 6.6. Mass (mg m^{-2}) = ears m^{-2} × grains/ear × grain weight (mg). We need to convert these figures to tonnes per hectare. There are 10^9 mg in a tonne and 10^4 m^2 in a hectare. Therefore

$$1 \text{ mg m}^{-2} = 10^4/10^9 = 10^{-5} \text{ t ha}^{-1}$$

so

$$\text{Weight (t ha}^{-1}) = 10^{-5} \times \text{weight (mg m}^{-2})$$

The results are shown in Table 6.13. It can be seen that the weight of grain on 24 July was much less dependent on seed rate than was the eventual yield which fell dramatically at high seed rates. The difference is probably related to the different

	Seed rate (m^{-2})					
	50	100	200	400	800	1600
Weight on 24 July (t ha^{-1})	7.58	9.34	9.84	7.66	6.56	5.57
Yield on 18 August (t ha^{-1})	9.51	9.65	7.81	5.63	4.19	2.79

Table 6.13. Relationship between the seed rate and (a) the weight of grain on 24 July 1990 and (b) the yield of grain obtained on 18 August 1990.

degrees of lodging at the different seed rates. At high seed rates almost all plants lodged by the time of harvest. This may have damaged the plants and made it easier for herbivores such as rabbits and pigeons to eat the grain. It would also have been far more difficult to harvest the grain, much of which may have been lost.

4. Farmers probably use high sowing rates because this gives them a 'factor of safety'. Even if most of their plants die they will still get a reasonable yield of wheat. Even so, this seems to be an example of farmers making choices which may not give the maximum mean profit. However, they may be minimising the chances of a totally disastrous year.

Problem 6.4

1. and 2. See Fig. 6.4, lines 1 and 2. Note: ignore irregularities at top and bottom, where few animals contribute to the value, compared to the bulk of animals contributing to central regions.

3. The LC$_{50}$ is the concentration at which the mortality is exactly 50 per cent. In this case values for *T. trifolii* (the herbivore) = 18 mg l^{-1}, while that for the predator *C. fransiscana* (its predator) = 10 mg l^{-1}. Note: adjusting for mortalities in the control group can be ignored.

4. The aphid herbivore suffers lower mortality from the pesticide than the predatory beetle. Possibly the herbivore is able to detoxify the pesticide via an oxidative enzyme pathway evolved to cope with secondary plant compounds. This is bad for herbivore control since there will be fewer predators to eat them.

5. See line 3 on Fig. 6.4. The LC$_{50}$ for *T. trifolii* on the 'Lahontan' variety = 8.5 mg l^{-1}.

6. The aphid pest, feeding on the 'Lahontan' variety of lucerne, is more susceptible to the pesticide malathion. This may be because the pest is in a poor condition due to an unsuitable food–plant, as suggested by the high mortality even in the control treatment when there is no malathion present. The pest is now of the same order of susceptibility to malathion as its predatory ladybird larva, and malathion treatment might be indicated if the pest outstripped its biological control agent.

7. See lines 4 and 5 on Fig. 6.4. The LC$_{50}$ for the herbivore is 42 mg l^{-1}, and for the predator is estimated by extrapolation to be 105 mg l^{-1}. Although pirimicarb is only effective on both pest and predator at higher concentrations than malathion (and is more expensive), it is selectively attacking the pest aphid rather than the predatory beetle. Because of its selective aphicidal action, pirimicarb would be the preferred chemical treatment in an IPM against the aphid *T. trifolii*.

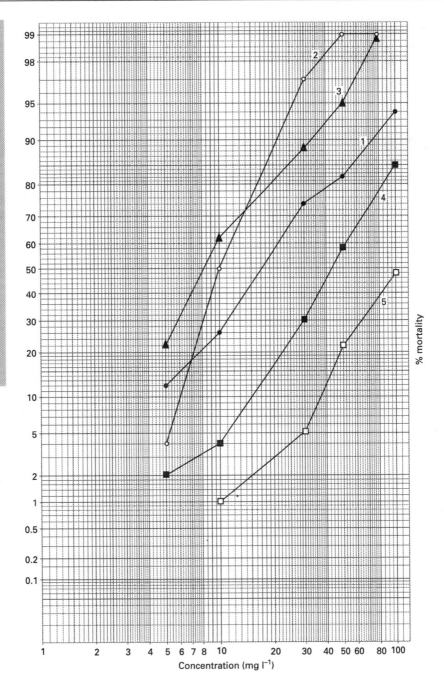

Figure 6.4. Cumulative mortality of insects exposed to insecticides. Line 1 = *T. trifolii* treated with malathion (closed circles). Line 2 = *C. fransiscana* treated with malathion (open circles). Line 3 = *T. trifolii* on Lahontan lucerne treated with malathion (closed triangles). Line 4 = *T. trifolii* treated with pirimicarb (closed squares). Line 5 = *C. fransiscana* treated with pirimicarb (open squares). LC_{50} values are found by determining the concentration at which each line crosses the 50% mortality (dashed lines).

Problem 7.1   Leakage of preservatives from a sawmill

Background

One of the main factors which gives rise to pollution by organic chemicals is their great mobility. In many cases pollutants are not deliberately released but gradually seep or leach away from areas in which they have accumulated. Fortunately, many organic chemicals are also relatively unstable and may be broken down by attack from micro-organisms. This often serves to detoxify them, but may, in some cases, give rise to more toxic breakdown products.

Further reading

Mellanby (1980).

Data and questions

A sawmill in Scotland produced pressure-treated timber for the building trade. All the timber was treated with a commercial preservative mixture made elsewhere by the chlorination of phenol. The three major groups of compounds in the preservative mixture were:

1. Chlorophenols (CPs).
2. Polychlorinated phenoxyphenols (PCPPs).
3. Polychlorinated dibenzofurans (PCDFs).

Each of these classes of compound are known to be toxic to many forms of life, and timber pressure-treated with a mixture of these compounds is resistant to fungal and insect attack for some years. Many thousands of litres of preservative were used in the 25 years prior to 1984 when the sawmill ceased operation. Leakage of preservatives over the years had resulted in considerable contamination of the soil around the site which was about 1 ha in area. After the sawmill ceased operation, the owners of the site started to monitor the contamination of the site. Soil cores were taken and the three major classes of compound analysed (Table 7.1). Because of the topography of the site all drainage from the site area entered a stream running alongside the sawmill and samples from that stream were analysed at intervals (Table 7.2).

1. Devise the best way to show the distribution profile for the three classes of compound in the soil in the 2 years for which data are presented.

2. What does this information tell you about the behaviour in the soil of the three classes of compound?

Table 7.1. Soil cores were removed from different parts of the site during December of each year. The average concentration of the major classes of compound was determined. n.d. = not detected.

| Core depth (cm) | Concentration (mg kg^{-1}) | | | | | |
| | 1984 samples | | | 1985 samples | | |
	CP	PCPP	PCDF	CP	PCPP	PCDF
0–5	146	9.3	15.8	1.5	1.6	9.5
5–20	132	2.8	7.6	0.5	0.5	3.0
20–40	95	0.2	1.2	5.0	n.d.	n.d.
40–60	69	n.d.	0.4	20.0	n.d.	0.1
60–80	51	n.d.	0.2	27.0	n.d.	n.d.
80–100	3	n.d.	n.d.	1.0	n.d.	n.d.
100–120	5	n.d.	n.d.	1.5	n.d.	n.d.
120–140	2	n.d.	n.d.	0.5	n.d.	n.d.

Table 7.2. The volume of water flowing in the stream at the point where it leaves the site was measured every 2 months throughout 1985 and the concentrations of the major classes of chemical were analysed in the water (in all cases the minimum concentration that could have been detected with the method used was 10 ng l^{-1}). n.d. = not detected.

| Month | Average flow of stream (m^3 min^{-1}) | Chemical concentration (mg l^{-1}) | | |
		CP	PCPP	PCDF
February	1.0	1.5	0.001	n.d.
April	0.75	1.75	0.0005	n.d.
June	0.5	2.0	n.d.	n.d.
August	0.75	2.5	n.d.	n.d.
October	0.75	1.5	n.d.	n.d.
December	1.0	1.0	n.d.	n.d.

3. Obviously the 1985 samples were less contaminated than the 1984 samples. Suggest the most likely ways in which the compounds could have been lost from the soil.

4. Using the information available to you, try to calculate the extent of the losses from each class of chemical by at least one of the routes you suggest. State clearly any assumptions you make and justify them.

5. The data you have been given in Tables 7.1 and 7.2 only allow you to estimate some of the losses. How would you determine experimentally the extent of the losses by the other routes you suggested in answer to question 3?

Extra information The dimensions of the sawmill site are approximately 66 × 150 m (= 1 ha). Due to site contamination and the remains of buildings and roads, the site is largely free of vegetation. The soil core analyses showed that the contamination was very uniform across the whole area.

The bulk density of the soil averages 1300 kg m^{-3} over the whole site and down to a depth of 1.5 m.

Problem 7.2   Heavy metal pollution and tolerance

Background

Heavy metals are another important pollutant which may result from mining activity, or from many areas of modern industry: large amounts of lead, for example, have until recently been added to petrol to improve its anti-knocking performance and have been expelled into the atmosphere. Many heavy metals are extremely toxic both to man and other organisms. Fortunately, however, many organisms seem to have developed mechanisms of tolerance, either by excluding the metals from their body or by storing them in a relatively safe form.

Further reading

Martin and Coughtrey (1982).

Data and questions

Tables 7.3–7.6 supply data on the levels of two heavy metal pollutants in the muddy deposits in four geographically separate estuaries in south-west England, and the effects on a common inhabitant of the estuarine mud-flats, the polychaete worm *Nereis diversicolor*.

1. Draw a graph to show the relationship between the concentration of each metal and its level in the worms and in the environment.

2. Is there any evidence of ion regulation for either metal?

3. Draw graphs to show the cumulative mortality of worms from the least and most polluted sites when exposed to 1 ppm copper or 50 ppm zinc.

4. From the graphs, estimate the median lethal times for worms from the two sites exposed to each metal.

5. What can you infer from those calculated values about the tolerance of the populations?

6. What can you infer from Tables 7.5 and 7.6 about the mechanisms of tolerance to the two metals?

7. What further work would be required to study the possibility of cross-tolerance to the two metals?

Table 7.3. Concentrations of copper and zinc in sediments and in bodies of *Nereis diversicolor* from four estuarine sites. Concentrations shown in ppm and $\log_{10}$ ppm.

| Site | Copper | | | | Zinc | | | |
| | Sediment | | Worm | | Sediment | | Worm | |
	ppm	$\log_{10}$	ppm	$\log_{10}$	ppm	$\log_{10}$	ppm	$\log_{10}$
1	18	1.26	20	1.30	92	1.96	151	2.18
2	296	2.47	116	2.06	2010	3.30	215	2.33
3	712	2.85	729	2.86	895	2.95	195	2.29
4	3500	3.54	922	2.96	2960	3.47	204	2.31

Table 7.4. Numbers of individual worms from four batches of 50 *Nereis diversicolor* from sites 1 and 4 dying in successive 12 hour periods when placed in 50% seawater containing 1 ppm copper or 50 ppm zinc.

| Hours from start | Deaths in 1 ppm Cu | | Deaths in 50 ppm Zn | |
	Site 1	Site 4	Site 1	Site 4
12	5	0	0	0
24	6	1	1	1
36	4	2	2	1
48	5	2	2	2
60	10	1	2	2
72	6	2	3	2
84	4	2	5	1
96	2	1	5	2
108	3	2	6	3
120	2	3	4	2
132	2	2	4	3
144	1	3	3	3
156		3	3	2
168		2	2	2
180		3	2	3
192		1	0	2
204		4	1	2
216		2	1	2
228		2	2	2
240		2	0	2
Survivors	0	10	4	9

Table 7.5. Initial concentrations of copper in the bodies of *Nereis diversicolor* from sites 1 and 4, and the median lethal times when exposed to 1 ppm copper in 50% seawater, when either taken fresh from the site (FIELD), or taken as tiny worms and reared for 6 months in copper-free 50% seawater (LAB).

Site	Type	Initial Cu (ppm)	Median lethal time (hours)
1	FIELD	16	40
	LAB	11	66
4	FIELD	882	147
	LAB	99	130

Table 7.6. Means (± standard errors) of the ^{65}Zn uptake by *Nereis diversicolor* from sites 1 and 4 when exposed for 30 days in 50% seawater containing 400 ppm non-radioactive zinc and 10 ppm radioactive zinc.

Day	Counts/minute	
	Site 1 worms	Site 4 worms
0	1 ± 1	1 ± 1
10	26 ± 13	11 ± 11
20	62 ± 16	33 ± 17
30	75 ± 17	40 ± 15

Problem 7.3   Lake diatoms as evidence of acidification

Background   The burning of sulphur-rich fossil fuels results in the release of sulphur dioxide gas which can combine with water in the atmosphere to produce dilute sulphuric acid. There has been much concern in recent years about the effects of the 'acid rain' which results. There have been reports of trees dying and lakes becoming acidified, particularly in upland regions with acid rocks where there is no buffering capacity to neutralise the acid. However, it has proved difficult to determine whether acid rain is actually the cause of these changes or whether other factors may be involved.

Further reading

Mason (1992: Ch. 7), Park (1987), Batterbee (1984), Batterbee *et al.* (1985).

Data and questions   This problem is about the use of diatoms in lake sediments as a record of the history of acidification. Other observations were taken to determine the probable cause of the acidification. The lake is Loch Enoch, a 50 ha freshwater lake 500 m above sea level, in south-west Scotland.

When lake diatoms die, they sink and their valves are preserved in the sediment. In oligotrophic acid lakes, sediments accumulate slowly, with recent acidification records held in the uppermost sediment. The sediment can be dated, using the radioisotopes ^{137}Cs or ^{210}Pb, so that the speed of acidification can be determined.

Diatom species are good indicators of pH, and Hustedt classified them as follows:

Alkalibiontic (alkbi):	occurring at pH >7
Alkaliphilous (alkph):	occurring at pH around 7, with widest distribution at pH >7
Circumneutral (cn):	with widest distribution at about pH 7
Acidophilous (acph):	occurring at pH around 7, with widest distribution at pH <7
Acidobiontic (acbi):	occurring at pH <7

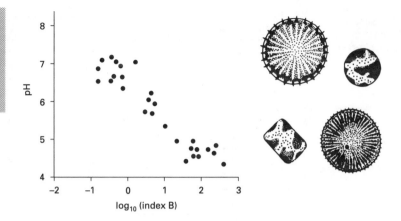

The ratio of the percentage occurrence of acid species to alkali species can be used to form an index of pH called index B. In index B the acidobiontic species are given a higher weighting than the acidophilous species, which in turn are weighted more than the circumneutral species. The alkali species are also weighted. The values of the weightings are derived from regression analyses.

$$\text{Index B} = \frac{\%cn + (5 \times \%acph) + (40 \times \%acbi)}{\%cn + (3.5 \times \%alkph) + (108 \times \%alkbi)}$$

Figure 7.1 shows the pH and $\log_{10}$(index B) values for 30 Scandinavian lakes.

1. From Fig. 7.1, find the regression formula which will allow you to estimate pH from an index B value. (Fit the line by eye.)

2. Draw a graph of the age of sediment against its depth below the surface layer (Table 7.7). Can the depth of the sediment sample be taken as a good guide to its age?

3. Estimate the pH of the lake at the time when each of the sediment samples in Table 7.8 was deposited, and draw a graph of estimated pH against sediment depth. Estimate when changes started to occur.

4. Based on the evidence in your graphs and in Tables 7.9 and 7.10, which of the four following hypotheses (a–d) is most likely to be true?

Table 7.7. Radioisotope dates of sediments.

Depth (cm)	^{210}Pb date
0	1981
5	1960
17.5	1900
25	1850
33.5	1800
50	(1700)

Table 7.8. Percentage of pH indicator diatoms in sediments.	Depth (cm)	% alkph	% cn	% acph	% acbi
	1	0.5	2	29	17
	2.5	0.5	3	30	15
	5	0	3	33	12
	11	0	6	37	7
	17.5	0.5	5	42	4
	25	1	12	35	4
	35	1	14	31	4
	45	0.5	14	33	3.5
	55	0.5	15	28	4
	65	0.5	13	31	4

Table 7.9. Percentage of pollen types in lake sediments.	Depth (cm)	% heather pollen	% grass pollen
	0	18	17
	5	17	15
	10	16	14
	15	19	13.5
	20	17.5	12.5
	25	17.5	12.5
	30	17.5	11.5
	35	20	11.5
	40	22	10
	45	19.5	9
	50	20	9
	55	20	9
	60	23	9
	65	22.5	9

Table 7.10. Heavy metal concentrations in sediments.	Depth (cm)	Pb (μg g^{-1})	Zn (μg g^{-1})	Cu (μg g^{-1})
	0	400	355	53
	10	370	190	43
	20	310	100	26
	30	155	120	8
	40	85	20	3
	50	105	35	30
	60	95	25	5

(a) Acidification of the lake is due to long-term changes.

(b) Acidification is due to afforestation in the late nineteenth and early twentieth centuries.

(c) Acidification is due to increased acid precipitation, principally from coal-burning industrial processes dating from the Industrial Revolution.

(d) Acidification is due to a reduction in grazing as a result of the reduction of upland farming. This decline would result in an increase in the formation of acid humus in soils. The grazing management in this area involves periodic burning of the vegetation, which encourages grasses, especially *Molinia caerulea* (purple moor grass), and keeps the heather young and palatable. Unfortunately, there are no good records of sheep or cattle numbers kept around the lake.

Problem 7.4 — Indicators of pollution in the river Mersey

Background

Pollution of rivers by sewage, farm waste and industry is still a major problem all over the world. It is clearly very important to monitor levels of pollution and this has been facilitated by sophisticated autoanalysis machines which are capable of detecting ever lower concentrations of pollutants. However, routine chemical monitoring has two disadvantages: it is not only very expensive but may also fail to detect pollution events which often occur only for a matter of hours. For this reason, methods of biological monitoring have been developed. The investigator simply takes samples of the organisms at particular sites and determines which species are present. It has been found that different species have different tolerances to pollution, so the nature of the catch can tell you a lot about the long-term state of the river: these organisms, after all, will 'detect' all pollution events because they live in the river all year round.

Further reading

Mellanby (1980), Mason (1991).

Data and questions

The river Mersey, above Irlam Weir (where the river joins the Manchester Ship Canal), receives water mostly from the rivers Tame, Etherow and Goyt, which arise in the Pennine range (see Fig. 7.2). In the 1980s, the Mersey catchment area was receiving outputs from many industrial works, and a large number of sewage treatment plants. Many of these plants were dealing with industrial wastes, and some were frequently overloaded. Table 7.11 gives the water chemistry at the five stations shown in Fig. 7.2. Figure 7.3 shows the concentrations of chromium, zinc and lead at several sites. Figure 7.4 shows the distribution of ten selected groups of invertebrates, fish and two species of aquatic mosses.

1. From the data in Table 7.11, which river is most polluted?

2. As far as is possible from the data provided, classify each of the river sections shown in Figure 7.5 into the following categories:

	Station				
	1 Tame	2 Etherow	3 Goyt	4 Mersey–Goyt	5 Mersey
Discharge	4.6	3.2	2.5	5.5	13.9
Suspended solids	34	17	26	19	47
Conductivity	617	347	415	395	544
Oxygen	84	91	94	87	75
BOD★	9.2	4.0	4.3	5.1	7.3
Total alkalinity	91	47	73	65	93
Cl	66	38	36	39	58
N in NH_3	1.9	0.5	0.9	0.8	2.2
N in NO_2	0.3	0.1	0.2	0.2	0.2
N in NO_3	4.2	2.5	2.1	2.8	3.5
P in PO_4	1.2	0.3	0.3	0.5	0.9

Table 7.11. Water chemistry in 1980 at five stations marked on map 1 (concentrations in mg l^{-1}, discharge in m^3 s^{-1}, conductivity in μS cm^{-1}, oxygen as % saturation).

★ Biological oxygen demand.

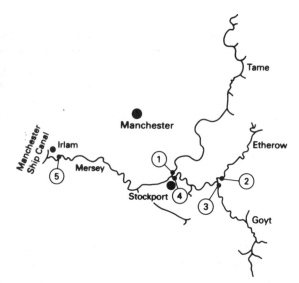

Figure 7.2. Map of the Mersey basin around Manchester, showing the five stations where water chemistry was measured. (From Holland and Harding, 1984.)

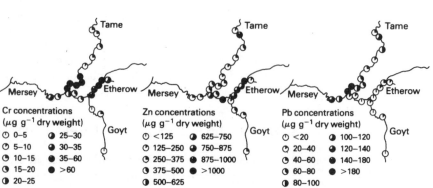

Figure 7.3. Concentrations of three heavy metals in shoot tips of the moss *Fontinalis antipyretica* at various sites in the Mersey basin. (From Holland and Harding, 1984.)

Cr concentrations
(μg g^{-1} dry weight)
- 0–5
- 5–10
- 10–15
- 15–20
- 20–25
- 25–30
- 30–35
- 35–60
- >60

Zn concentrations
(μg g^{-1} dry weight)
- <125
- 125–250
- 250–375
- 375–500
- 500–625
- 625–750
- 750–875
- 875–1000
- >1000

Pb concentrations
(μg g^{-1} dry weight)
- <20
- 20–40
- 40–60
- 60–80
- 80–100
- 100–120
- 120–140
- 140–180
- >180

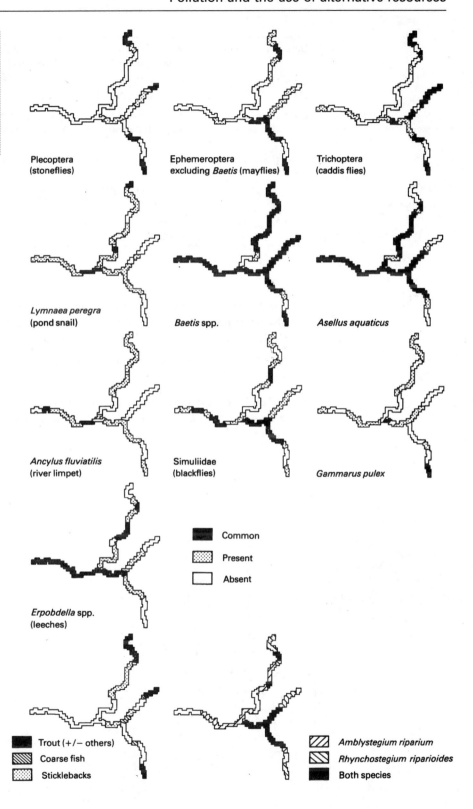

Figure 7.4. Distribution of several species of invertebrates, fish and mosses in the Mersey basin. (From Holland and Harding, 1984.)

Plecoptera (stoneflies)

Ephemeroptera excluding *Baetis* (mayflies)

Trichoptera (caddis flies)

Lymnaea peregra (pond snail)

Baetis spp.

Asellus aquaticus

Ancylus fluviatilis (river limpet)

Simuliidae (blackflies)

Gammarus pulex

Erpobdella spp. (leeches)

Common
Present
Absent

Trout (+/− others)
Coarse fish
Sticklebacks

Amblystegium riparium
Rhynchostegium riparioides
Both species

Class 1A	Good	Water of high quality suitable for drinking supply abstractions; game or other high class fisheries; high amenity value.
Class 1B	Good	Water of less high quality than class 1A but usable for substantially the same purposes.
Class 2	Fair	Water suitable for drinking supply after advanced treatment; supporting reasonably good coarse fisheries; moderate amenity value.
Class 3	Poor	Waters which are polluted to an extent that fish are absent or only sporadically present; may be used for low grade industrial abstraction purposes; considerable potential for further use if cleaned up.
Class 4	Bad	Waters which are grossly polluted and are likely to cause nuisance.

3. Classify the ten groups of invertebrates in Fig. 7.4 into (a) those which are least tolerant of organic pollution, (b) those which are most tolerant and (c) those which are intermediate or of little value in indicating organic pollution.

4. Describe the evidence for susceptibility to heavy metal pollution in *one* named invertebrate group.

5. Explain how organic pollution affects the distribution of the mosses *Amblystegium riparium* and *Rhynchostegium riparioides*. Both species are known to be tolerant of heavy metal pollution.

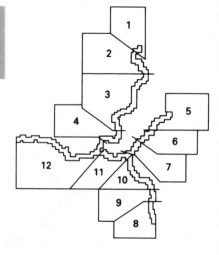

Figure 7.5. River sections of the Mersey basin. (From Holland and Harding, 1984.)

6. Salmon fisheries disappeared in the early 1800s from the Mersey and its northern tributary, the Irwell (which also now enters the Manchester Ship Canal). What prevents the return of salmon?

Problem 7.5 — Feasibility of wind power generation

Background

As we have seen in Chapter 3, it is becoming clear that burning fossil fuels is causing pollution on a global scale. There are also major pollution problems with the major alternative, nuclear energy; radioactive waste is very difficult to contain and extremely expensive to reprocess and store. Many of the early power stations are being decommissioned and few new ones being built. There is therefore renewed interest in 'alternative' energy sources such as solar, wave and wind power. Of these, wind power is the most immediately practicable and is being promoted world-wide. The main problems are that wind is a dilute and unpredictable form of energy.

Further reading

Cheremisinoff (1978).

Data and questions

The habitable area of the UK is approximately 288 000 km^2. There are approximately 20×10^6 homes. At any one time 750 kW of power is used per 200 homes. Non-domestic needs are to be catered for to the extent of three times domestic needs.

A feasibility study is initiated to see whether it would be possible to generate the total amount of power required using wind turbines. Because wind turbines absorb energy their minimum distance apart has to be roughly ten times their height. It is proposed to use a grid of turbines each generating 500 kW at a wind speed of 8 m s^{-1} and each 40 m high. Power generated is proportional to the cube of the wind speed.

1. How much power is needed and how many turbines are required?

2. What proportion of the UK usable land would the grid cover?

3. Given your calculation, the map supplied (Fig. 7.6) and your knowledge of the topography of the country, would reliance on wind power be a practical proposition?

4. Energy storage and distribution would be necessary to allow for fluctuations in wind; how could this be arranged? Discuss the possible environmental impact of such a proposal.

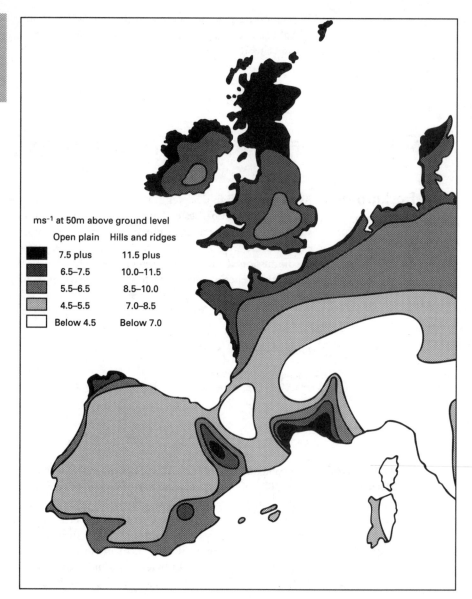

Figure 7.6. Europe's wind resources: map showing mean wind speeds over western Europe.

ms⁻¹ at 50m above ground level

Open plain	Hills and ridges
7.5 plus	11.5 plus
6.5–7.5	10.0–11.5
5.5–6.5	8.5–10.0
4.5–5.5	7.0–8.5
Below 4.5	Below 7.0

Solutions

Problem 7.1

1. To show changes most clearly the distribution profiles are best laid out as in Fig. 7.7, with depth on the *y*-axis and concentration on the *x*-axis. The 2 years can be shown as different coloured bars (as here) or on different sides of the *y*-axis.

2. Figure 7.1 shows that CPs are fairly mobile in the soil. They leach downwards and the peak concentration occurs lower down in the profile after a year.
   It is clear that PCPPs are immobile in the soil since their distribution in the soil remains unchanged but they appear to be unstable, since only a small fraction remains after a year. The rest has probably been broken down.
   Like the PCPPs, PCDFs are immobile and their distribution in the profile remains unchanged, but they seem to be more stable since a greater fraction remains after a year.

3. Compounds were probably lost by leaching (especially CPs), breakdown by micro-organisms (especially PCPPs and PCDFs) and possibly by evaporation.

4. To calculate the losses of each class of chemical one must determine the amounts present in 1984 and 1985. To do this the soil concentration of chemical in each depth class must be multiplied by the mass of soil in that class.

Figure 7.7. Distribution of three chemicals in the soil from a sawmill in 1984 (open) and 1985 (shaded).

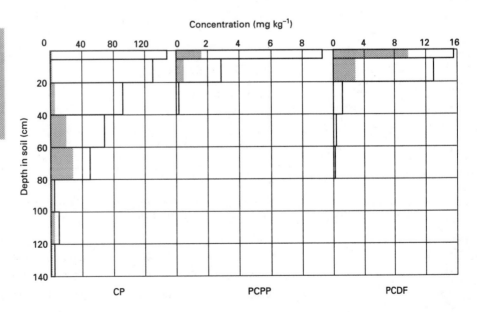

The area of the site is 10^4 m^2 so the volume of soil is

0–5 cm = $10^4 \times 0.05 = 500$ m^3
5–20 cm = $10^4 \times 0.15 = 1500$ m^3
20–40 cm, etc. = $10^4 \times 0.20 = 2000$ m^3

The mass of soil in each depth class is volume × density so

0–5 cm = $500 \times 1.3 \times 10^3 = 6.5 \times 10^5$ kg
5–20 cm = $1500 \times 1.3 \times 10^3 = 1.95 \times 10^6$ kg
20–40 cm, etc. = $2000 \times 1.3 \times 10^3 = 2.60 \times 10^6$ kg

The initial mass of CPs, therefore, is as follows:

$$6.5 \times 10^5 \{146 + (3 \times 132) + [4 \times (95 + 69 + 51 + 3 + 5 + 2)]\} \text{ mg}$$
$$= 6.5 \times 10^5 (146 + 396 + 900) \text{ mg}$$
$$= 9.38 \times 10^8 \text{ mg}$$
$$= 938 \text{ kg}$$

The final mass of CPs is

$$6.5 \times 10^5 \{1.5 + (3 \times 0.5) + [4 \times (5 + 20 + 27 + 1 + 1.5 + 0.5)]\}$$
$$= 6.5 \times 10^5 \times 223$$
$$= 1.45 \times 10^8 \text{ mg}$$
$$= 145 \text{ kg}$$

The amount lost over the time equals $938 - 145 = 793$ kg.

Similarly:

Initial mass of PCPPs = 12.0 kg

Final mass = 2.0 kg

Amount lost = 10.0 kg

Initial mass of PCDFs = 29.8 kg

Final mass = 12.3 kg

Amount lost = 17.5 kg

Losses of each chemical by leaching of water can be calculated on the basis of two assumptions:
1. that the water flow is constant over each 2-month period.
2. that the concentration of the chemical is also constant.

Additionally each 2-month period is assumed to last for 60 days.
The total volume flow of water over each period is the flow rate multiplied by the time of flow. There are $60 \times 24 \times 60$ min in 60 days so:

Volume flow = Flow rate × 60 × 24 × 60 = Flow rate × 86 400

The amount of chemical lost is

Volume flow × concentration

However, concentrations are given in milligrams per litre. Since there are 1000 mg in a gram and 1000 l in a cubic metre

$$1 \text{ mg l}^{-1} = 1 \text{ g m}^{-3}$$

Amount lost, therefore, is

(86 400 × flow rate × concentration) g

The amount of CPs lost by leaching, therefore, is

$$86\,400 \times [(1 \times 1.5) + (0.75 \times 0.75) + (0.5 \times 2.0) + (0.5 \times 2.5) +$$

$$(0.75 \times 1.5) + (1 \times 1)] \text{ g}$$

$$= 86\,400 \times 7.15 \text{ g}$$

$$= 617\,760 \text{ g}, = 620 \text{ kg to two significant figures}$$

This makes up $620/793 \times 100 = 78$ per cent of the total loss of CPs.

The amount of PCPPs lost by leaching is

$$86\,400 \times [(1 \times 0.001) + (0.75 \times 0.0005)]$$

$$= 118.8 \text{ g}, = 120 \text{ g to two significant figures}$$

This makes up $120/10\,000 \times 100 = 1.2$ per cent of the total loss of PCPPs.

Negligible amounts of PCDFs were lost by leaching.

5. To determine losses by breakdown of chemicals by bacteria one would measure the concentration of breakdown products in the soil.

Problem 7.2   1. See Fig. 7.8. (Note that log forms of the data are used.)

2. There is little evidence for ion regulation of copper – the relatively lower concentration in worms occurring where there are higher copper concentrations in the sediment could be due to sampling differences – the worms may live deep in the sediment, whereas copper may be present only in the surface layers of sediment. There is strong evidence of zinc regulation by the worms – the zinc concentration in the worms is almost independent of the concentration of zinc in the sediment.

3. See Fig. 7.9.

4. Lethal times for 50 per cent of the populations are:

Copper, site 1: 54 hours   Zinc, site 1: 108 hours
Copper, site 4: 154 hours   Zinc, site 4: 162 hours

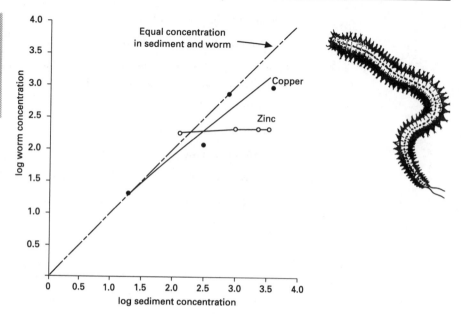

Figure 7.8.
Relationship between
the concentrations of
copper (●) and zinc
(○) in sediment and in
worms.

5. Worms from the least copper polluted site are less tolerant (die faster) than worms from the most copper polluted site, when exposed to 1 ppm Cu. Worms from the least zinc polluted site are less tolerant (die faster) than worms from the most zinc polluted site, when exposed to 50 ppm Zn.

6. As you can see from Table 7.5, animals from the high copper site are less susceptible to copper poisoning, irrespective of conditions of rearing. Therefore there appears to be congenital, possibly genetic, copper tolerance at that site. From Table 7.6, animals from the high zinc site accumulate zinc significantly more slowly than animals from the less zinc polluted site. Therefore zinc tolerance may be based on either decreased rate of uptake or increased rate of excretion.

7. Testing for cross-tolerance would involve two pairs of experiments. In one, the tolerance to 1 ppm Cu would be compared in animals from a low copper, high zinc site and animals from a low copper, low zinc site. In the other, the tolerance to 50 ppm Zn would be compared in animals from a low zinc, high copper site and animals from a low zinc, low copper site. The experimental protocol would follow that for the animals in Table 7.4. The four sites must have reproductively isolated populations. Sites 1 and 2 would be suitable for the first set of trials, but there is no high copper, low zinc site among the four listed which is suitable for the second set.

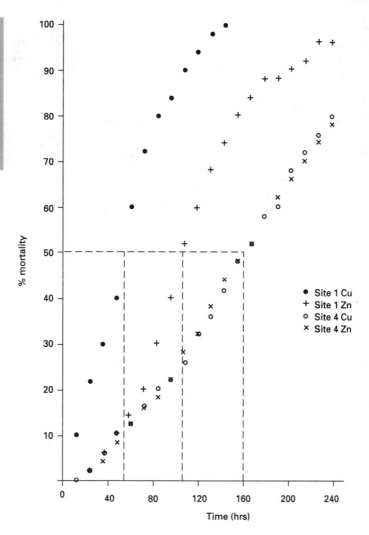

Figure 7.9. Cumulative mortality of worms from sites 1 and 4 over time when placed in 50 per cent seawater containing 1 ppm copper or 50 ppm zinc. Dashed lines show lethal times for 50% of the populations.

Problem 7.3

1. From the graph (Fig. 7.10), the intercept is at pH 6.40, and the slope is −0.85, i.e. the line increases by 1 unit of $\log_{10}$(index B) for a fall of 0.85 in pH. Thus the regression is pH = 6.40 − 0.85[$\log_{10}$(index B)].

2. The data of age against depth of sediment (Fig. 7.11) fit a straight line well, so depth is a good indication of age.

3. Fitting the data for the top layer of sediment,

Depth (cm)	% alkph	% cn	% acph	% acbi
1	0.5	2	29	17

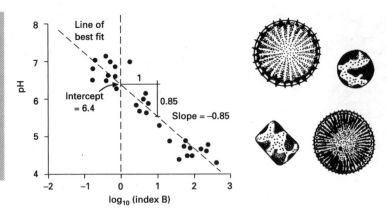

Figure 7.10. The relationship between $\log_{10}$(index B) of diatoms and the pH of the lakes in which they are found. A line of best fit has been drawn which has a slope of –0.85 and crosses the x-axis at a pH value of 6.4.

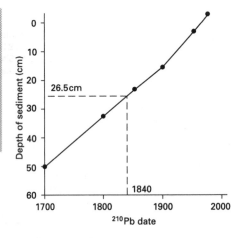

Figure 7.11. The relationship between the depth of sediment in Loch Enoch and its date derived from ^{210}Pb analysis. Sediment found at a depth of 26.5 cm appears to age from 1840.

into the formula,

$$\text{Index B} = \frac{\%cn + (5 \times \%acph) + (40 \times \%acbi)}{\%cn + (3.5 \times \%alkph) + (108 \times \%alkbi)}$$

gives us

$$\text{Index B} = [2 + (5 \times 29) + (40 \times 17)]/[2 + (3.5 \times 0.5)]$$

$$= (2 + 145 + 680)/(2 + 1.75) = 827/3.75 = 220.533$$

From the equation pH = 6.40 − [0.85 × log(index B)],

$$\text{pH} = 6.40 - (0.85 \times \log 220.533)$$

$$= 6.40 - (0.85 \times 2.3435) = 6.40 - 1.99 = 4.41$$

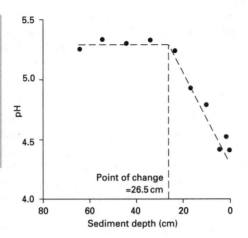

Figure 7.12. The relationship between sediment depth and the estimated pH of Loch Enoch. There appears to be a sudden change occurring at a depth of 26.5 cm after which the pH starts to fall.

Working out the pH for the other samples gives us:

Depth (cm)	1	2.5	5	11	17.5	25	35	45	55	65
Est. pH	4.41	4.53	4.42	4.80	4.92	5.25	5.32	5.29	5.32	5.25

These are used in Fig. 7.12 which appears to have two straight-line segments: the intersection of the segments at 26.5 cm depth suggests that pH was steady until about 1830–40, and dropped rapidly thereafter.

4. The advent of acidification in 1830–40 precludes hypothesis (a) (that acidification is due to long-term change), because the change is too recent. It also precludes hypothesis (b) (acidification is due to afforestation in the late nineteenth and early twentieth centuries), because the change occurs earlier.

   The timing of the change is consistent with the Industrial Revolution (hypothesis (c)), but could also be consistent with the time of a change in land use (hypothesis (d)), if such a change did occur. Tables 7.9 and 7.10 allow us to choose between these two hypotheses, for the following reasons.

   Although there are no records of grazing around the lake, there are pollen records in the deposits. These show a change in the proportions of heather and grass pollen falling into the lake from the surrounding land. However, whereas an increase in heather pollen and a decrease in grass pollen would be expected if the land had stopped being regularly grazed and burnt, the reverse trend has occurred. This suggests that the land has become *more* exploited for grazing, thus there should be *less* formation of acid humus, so change in land use cannot explain the increase in acidification. Therefore we are left with hypothesis (c). The increase in heavy metal deposition at about the time of the change in diatom communities can be accounted for by increased deposition from the atmosphere. This supports the argument that the acidification is caused by acid deposition from the atmosphere.

Problem 7.4

1. The Tame is the most polluted: it carries more suspended solids, more total dissolved solids (conductivity), is less saturated with oxygen, has higher biochemical oxygen demand (a bioassay measure of the amount of oxidisable organic compounds), highest nitrates, nitrites and ammonia, highest phosphates and chloride. (Not surprising, since for most of its length it passes through heavily populated and industrialised areas.)

2. and 3. (This looks like a two-sided problem: we cannot classify the river sections (question 2) until we know which are the tolerant organisms, and we cannot rank the organisms by tolerance without knowing the pollution status of the different sections of the rivers (question 3). It certainly helps to know something about the biology of the organisms: for example, that stoneflies and mayflies (except *Baetis* spp.) are the benthic invertebrates least tolerant of pollution. Without that kind of knowledge, we can, however, find several strong clues: the distribution of trout is given, and we are told that only water of class 1A or B will support game fish (which include trout). Also, we would expect that headwaters will not be organically polluted, and pollution will increase downstream, although downstream of a pollution source the river will recover by dilution from side tributaries and aeration. We will therefore chip away at questions 2 and 3 together.)

The headwaters of the Tame, Etherow and Goyt (sections 1, 5 and 8) are the least polluted − that is where game fisheries (trout) and stoneflies occur. Conversely, area 9 on the Goyt and area 4 on the Tame appear most polluted, because, of the organisms we are told about, only the water hoglouse *Asellus* occurs in 9 and leeches *Erpobdella* in 9 and 4.

At the same time, we have assigned Plecoptera and Ephemeroptera to the highest ranks of susceptibility and *Asellus* and *Erpobdella* to the lowest ranks.

What can we make of the remaining species and sections? Looking at the patterns in Fig. 7.4, Trichoptera resemble Plecoptera, but seem more tolerant. Conversely, simuliid larvae tend to follow the pattern of the tolerant *Asellus*, while *Baetis* nymphs are so tolerant and widespread as to have little predictive power. The three remaining species, *Lymnaea*, *Ancylus* and *Gammarus*, are widespread but sporadic: the absence of the two mollusc species from the Etherow may be attributable to the low alkalinity, which would make shell formation difficult, or to some factor which is unstated, e.g. fast flow rate (suggested by the low level of suspended solids).

We can now attempt to *rank* the sections:

> Least polluted 1, 5, 8
> Intermediate 2, 3, 6, 7, 10, 11, 12
> Most polluted 9, then 4

and *rank* the invertebrates:

Least tolerant	Plecoptera
Slightly tolerant	Ephemeroptera and Trichoptera
Tolerant but sporadic	*Lymnaea, Ancylus, Gammarus*
Tolerant and widely common	*Erpobdella*, simuliids
Most tolerant	*Asellus, Baetis*

That answers question 3. For question 2 we still need to assign sections to classes.

Sections 1, 2, 5 and 8 support game fisheries and thus are in class 1. The chromium and zinc contamination in section 2 puts this at the bottom of this group – perhaps in class 1B.

Sections 9 and 4 support no fish, not even sticklebacks, and thus are in class 4 (or the bottom of class 3).

The remaining sections are in class 2 or 3: coarse fisheries are present in sections 7 and 10, suggesting they are in class 2.

The remaining sections (3, 6, 11, 12) support only sticklebacks, or no fish. They are not, however, so species poor as to warrant class 4, so class 3 appears apt.

In summary therefore:

Section	1	2	3	4	5	6	7	8	9	10	11	12
Class	1A	1B	3	4	1A	3	2	1A	4	2	3	3

4. The Trichoptera show evidence of heavy metal susceptibility: their anomalous absence from sections 2 and 6 suggest that they are intolerant of the high metal contaminations there.

5. Both species of aquatic moss are absent from the most polluted areas (sections 4 and 9). Neither species is present at the top of the Etherow, i.e. at very low organic pollution levels. Thus both species need some organic pollution, but not too much.

   Both species occur in the seven sections classed as 1B, 2 or 3, except in section 12, a class 3 section in which only *Rhynchostegium* occurs. Only *Rhynchostegium* occurs in section 4 (class 4 or bottom of class 3 – this gives some retrospective support for removing section 4 from class 4): thus *Rhynchostegium* appears more tolerant than *Amblystegium*. *Amblystegium* occurs in two of the three class 1A sections, *Rhynchostegium* in only one of them: thus *Amblystegium* comes in first as pollution increases.

6. Although salmon might spawn in the headwaters of the Mersey tributaries in their present state, they could not reach them. The reasons are two-fold: first, the mechanical obstructions of weirs, etc. would need to be circumvented, but, secondly, and more seriously, the poor to bad conditions of the lower reaches would render them impassable. (The situation is even worse further downstream, in the Ship Canal, where long sections are class 4.)

Problem 7.5 1. The power required for domestic use is equal to the power required per home multiplied by the number of homes. Therefore

$$\text{Domestic power} = (750/200) \times 20 \times 10^6 \text{ kW}$$

$$= 7.5 \times 10^7 \text{ kW}$$

Non-domestic needs are three times domestic needs. Therefore the total power required is four times the domestic needs:

$$\text{Total power} = 7.5 \times 10^7 \times 4 = 3.0 \times 10^8 \text{ kW}$$

If each turbine produces 500 kw then the number required is

$$3.0 \times 10^8/500 = 6.0 \times 10^5$$

2. If each turbine is 40 m high then turbines must be 400 m apart. Each turbine will therefore take up a space of

$$400 \text{ m} \times 400 \text{ m} = 1.6 \times 10^5 \text{ m}^2 = 0.16 \text{ km}^2$$

The turbines would therefore take up an area of

$$6.0 \times 10^5 \times 0.16 = 1.0 \times 10^5 \text{ km}^2$$

This constitutes $(1 \times 10^5/2.88 \times 10^5) \times 100 = 35$ per cent of the total.

3. The map shows that around a third to a half of the UK (mainly in Scotland and Northern Ireland) receives winds strong enough (8 m s^{-1}) to power wind turbines if positioned on open plains, while in the rest turbines could receive enough power if positioned on hills and ridges. Enough turbines could therefore theoretically be sited in the UK to produce its electricity. However, those areas which can produce adequate wind are also the areas which are most remote from centres of population and most inaccessible. They also tend to be mountainous regions on which siting of windmills would be difficult and which are likely to suffer from potentially damaging gales. It would probably prove extremely costly to build and provide access to the huge grid of windmills and to provide maintenance.

4. The best way the electricity industry has found to store energy is to use the gravitational potential energy bound up in water in a series of reservoirs. During periods of peak production water is pumped up to a higher reservoir, and at times of peak demand water flows down again, driving turbines. This system could be operated in Scotland where the country is mountainous and where suitable reservoirs could be built by damming glaciated valleys. However, the energy storage required for a single day's supply is power times time which is

$$3.0 \times 10^8 \times 60 \times 60 \times 24 \text{ kJ} = 2.6 \times 10^{13} \text{ kJ}$$

The gravitational potential energy an object possesses (in joules) is $9.8 \times \text{mass} \times \text{height}$. If water is raised by 100 m, the mass of water required to store 2.6×10^{13} kJ is therefore

$$\text{Mass} = 2.6 \times 10^{13} \times 1000/(9.8 \times 100)$$

$$= 2.7 \times 10^{13} \text{ kg}$$

Since the density of water is 1000 kg m^{-3} this equals a volume of $2.7 \times 10^{10} \text{ m}^3$. Two huge lakes will be required. Even if the mean depth is 30 m the area of each lake will have to be around 10^9 m^2 or approximately 30×30 km. If storage is required for a week's use *fourteen* of these huge lakes will be required.

Clearly such a storage scheme would be a huge engineering undertaking and would have a massive impact on the area in which it was sited. The Highlands of Scotland are an important semi-natural environment. Such massive schemes would have little chance of being accepted. The windmills themselves, together with their access roads, would also have an unacceptable impact on the environment and the windmills themselves would prove intrusive in this 'wilderness'.

MANAGING THE ENVIRONMENT

CONSERVATION AND ENVIRONMENTAL IMPACT ASSESSMENT

The management plan for a nature reserve

Background
This problem illustrates how the environmental biologist puts his or her knowledge to use in evaluating the existing conservation of an area, and drawing up a plan for managing it, whether the plan be to maintain an area of high value, enhance an area of lesser value or create a new conservation area. Managing nature reserves, rather than 'letting nature take its course', may appear to be a strange idea, but is necessary if the purpose is to conserve something specific, usually in quite a small area. Few areas in the British Isles have not been managed for some purpose at some time – including most of the so-called ancient woodlands.

As with many of the problems in this chapter, there is no single right answer: instead the problem calls for the reasonable application of knowledge and understanding. Table 8.1 provides a checklist of things to consider when preparing a management prescription for a nature reserve.

Further reading

Tait *et al.* (1988), Green (1981: Ch. 10).

Data and question
Heysham Nature Reserve (Fig. 8.1) is an area of about 8 ha on the coast of Morecambe Bay, between the nuclear power station and the local town and port. The adjacent coast is important for coastal birds. Currently the reserve is managed by Nuclear Electric, as a relatively inexpensive amenity offering quiet recreation to the local community. Its potential as an educational resource for local schools will be increased by the opening of a classroom. Local volunteers have produced good species lists of the birds, insects and flora, and undertake maintenance supported by the company.

Some current problems include:

1. Noise and visual disturbance from heavy traffic using Princess Alexandra Way;

2. Vehicle access is from a quiet back road, Moneyclose Lane, and vehicles can leave the roads and carpark on the reserve, encouraging fly-tipping;

3. Access from the power station end is via a steep path with steps;

Table 8.1. Management Prescription Checklist for Nature Reserves	**1. General description** include map (with scale) history descriptions of individual parts climate hydrology/hydrography geology topography/landscape (sense of space, water bodies, greenness) intended use of areas (conservation, recreation, education, timber, etc.)

2. Evaluation criteria
size of proposed reserve
diversity – physical, botanical, animal
naturalness
rarity – of species, of habitats
fragility
typicalness
recorded history
intrinsic appeal
position in an ecological unit
potential value
accessibility (lesser sites may be an important resource for the local community)

3. General management aims
geology
topography
vegetation types
communities and populations
education and research

4. To what constraints is the area subject?
natural constraints, e.g. erosion, seral succession
man-induced, e.g. eutrophication, pollution, tree management
external, e.g. green corridors, pollution
legal and other obligations, e.g. footpaths, property, reserve status, safety (mineshafts, rocks, water, fire, trees), access, tenure
management, e.g. staffing, time, funding

5. Rationales for objectives

6. Management prescriptions, ranked by priority
routine prescriptions, e.g. control damage, maximise potential, staffing
obligatory prescriptions, e.g. public rights of way, conform to reserve regulations, protection of persons
priority prescriptions, e.g. improve and monitor quality, extend habitats, maintain sites, maintain populations
prescriptions to meet desirable objectives
prescriptions to meet intended uses, e.g. education, research

7. Monitoring effectiveness of measures

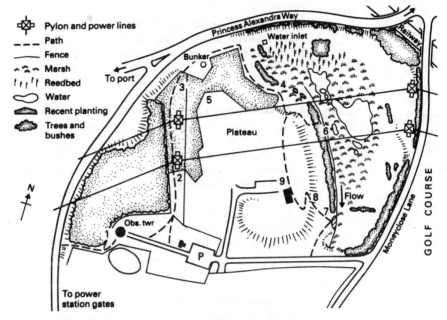

Figure 8.1. Map of Heysham Nature Reserve.

4. The open-water area is rapidly silting up, and tall marsh vegetation is encroaching round the sides (the sluice controlling water flow is accessible downstream of the reserve);

5. Eutrophication may be caused by surface runoff from the golf course on the other side of Moneyclose Lane;

6. The central 'plateau' on which the classroom is sited contains large amounts of basic rubble, mostly pulverised fuel ash (PFA) and soil has been imported and spread over the northern end;

7. The build-up of dead undergrowth, especially on the north side, poses a potential fire risk;

8. Heavy machinery cannot operate beneath the twin power lines which cross the site;

9. The map and notes obtained from the Visitors' Centre at the power station (reproduced in box on pp. 141–143) are the only guidance available for visitors.

INFORMATION NOTES ON THE ROUTE THROUGH THE RESERVE
Numbers refer to numbered positions on the map (Fig. 8.1)

1. Near observation tower. From here we look down on an important area (shown stippled on map) of gorse, hawthorn and brambles. Splashes of red campion can be seen in the central glade, while in late summer the pink areas are rosebay willowherb. Linnets and greenfinches nest in the gorse and can be seen flying around. You can also see and hear dunnocks, wrens, song thrushes and whitethroats. Large numbers of migrants pass through these bushes and scientific ringing is carried out by the Morecambe Bay Ringing Group under licence from the British Trust for Ornithology. You may see small white, large white and wall butterflies below, while behind you on the short grass may be small heath butterflies. The pale blue harebells flower around the perimeter in July.

2. South entry to pylon bank path. Above this path is gorse to the west and below is a mixed tree community to the east, including hawthorn and a valuable collection of willows. Between the trees are plants like dog daisy, yarrow, thistles and scabious, growing with sorrel and grasses which include Yorkshire fog. Butterflies around here include the large skipper and small copper, and you may also see small tortoiseshell, wall, meadow brown and small heath.

3. Far end of pylon bank path. The nettle patch, knapweed, fleabane and other flowers here are important for the small tortoiseshell butterflies. The trees at the end of the path include alder and hawthorn, which are valuable food sources for the larvae of many moths and other insects. The concrete bunker is a Second World War gun-post.

4. Bulrush corner. The reeds and bulrushes (or, more correctly, reedmaces) in the marsh are spreading to cover a larger area and have to be managed. The marsh provides valuable nesting habitat for sedge warblers, moorhen, mallard, reed bunting and water rail. Plants which provide colour in the marsh are purple loosestrife and, around the edges, stands of yellow fleabane. On the drier area above the path you may see silver Y moths hovering near the coltsfoot, which has yellow flowers in February and masses of large round leaves later on.

5. Transplanted patches. Patches of ground have been transplanted from nearby areas, including the coastal duneland reserve at Silverdale. They contain plants like yellow rattle, broomrape, cowslip, black medick and mayweed. The mound of rocks near by has some interesting plants growing on it, such as yellow toadflax, wild pansy, common vetch and broom. On the flatter ground can be seen small pink common centaury flowers, while you will probably see many small dark wolf spiders running away. Meadow pipits are common here and there is usually a covey of partridges in the vicinity.

6. By the screened observation platform in the willows, looking over the marsh. Flowers of the marsh: kingcup, water horsetail, sedges, rushes, cuckoo flower, celery-leaved crowfoot, marsh thistle, fleabane and marsh pennywort. In the distance you may see the pale pink flowering rush which was originally rescued from the development site across the road. You will probably see or hear mallard, moorhen, snipe, sedge warbler, reed bunting and water rail. Other birds will be in the willow, such as willow warblers and goldfinches. Blue and red damselflies can be seen flying and perching among the marsh plants, while raft spiders scuttle over the wet vegetation in pursuit of their prey – flies and smaller creatures.

7. Dipping pond. The plants in the pond and the stream include great willowherb, burr-reed, Canadian pondweed, water plantain, celery-leaved crowfoot, crowfoot, amphibious bistort, yellow flag and duckweed. On drier ground are common spotted orchids, yellow and white melitots and horsetails. In the pond you may see sticklebacks, common newts, pond and ramshorn snails, water mites, water boatmen, whirligig beetles and diving beetles, while common darter dragonflies and red damselflies fly above it. On the drier area above the pond are common blue, small heath, wall and small copper butterflies.

8. On zig-zag path by platform. The colony of burnet moths is centred here, among the birdsfoot trefoil, knapweed, thistles, docks and rosebay willowherb. You can also see common blue, small copper, wall, meadow brown, small heath, small tortoiseshell and even migrant red admiral butterflies here. The bushes with yellow flowers are gorse and broom, and watch out for the small yellow shell moth.

9. By the classroom. Growing low on the ground are several leguminous plants such as alsike clover, melitots, black medick and birdsfoot trefoil. There are also common mallow, purple toadflax, common centaury and eyebright to watch out for. Burnet and silver Y moths feed on the flowers, as do wall, meadow brown, small tortoiseshell and small heath butterflies. Many small pale grass moths can be seen among the short vegetation, where they may be eaten by the ever-present meadow pipits.

Design a management plan for Heysham Nature Reserve for a 5-year period. Divide the reserve into appropriate habitat areas and provide the following information for each:

1. Name of habitat area.
2. Assessment of habitat area (refer in your answer to the notes provided for visitors, above).
3. Management objectives.
4. Management prescription.
5. Priority.
6. Time-scale (start and end dates, continuous or staged, etc.).

Finally, use these headings to formulate an assessment of the reserve as a whole.

For this exercise, assume that financial support from the company would include reasonable costs of maintaining boundaries, paths and buildings, and supply of materials and plants and supporting literature. Labour, other than that used in the above activities, is to be supplied by volunteers. The management prescription should fit into these constraints, but a costing exercise is not required.

Problem 8.2 — The size and conservation value of woods

Background   Since the Second World War there has been a steady destruction of natural habitats such as woods, heaths and marshes to make way for housing, roads, industry, leisure and, most importantly, farming. Natural habitats have been either totally destroyed, reduced in size or fragmented. This has had a bad effect on conservation: organisms now exist in increasingly small 'islands' of suitable habitat in a 'sea' of inhospitable land. Classical biogeographical studies on real islands show that such small, isolated islands are unable to sustain such a great diversity of organisms as large adjacent ones. Similar biogeographical studies on natural habitats can help us design an effective strategy of habitat protection and creation for conservation.

Further reading

Green (1981: Chs 1 and 7).

Data and questions

This problem investigates the results of a survey carried out in the early 1970s (Moore and Hooper 1975) which examined the distribution of 54 species of birds in woods of different sizes. The 433 woods sampled offered a wide range of habitat types and were situated all over the British Isles.

Table 8.2 shows the frequency with which five passerine species are found in woods of different areas.

The experimenters also investigated the way in which the numbers of species in woods varied with their area. It was found that the data best fitted the McArthur and Wilson (1967) island equilibrium model in which woods are treated as 'islands' of suitable habitat in a 'sea' of unsuitable open country. According to this model

$$S = C\,A^{K} \tag{1}$$

Table 8.2. Frequency of five passerines in woods of different areas.

Species	Percentage of woods of each area category inhabited by the species					
Area category (hectares)	0.001–0.01	0.01–0.1	0.1–1.0	1.0–10.0	10.0–100.0	≥ 100.0
Blackbird (*Turdus merula*)	13	34	63	72	91	100
House sparrow (*Passer domesticus*)	9	20	44	22	27	35
Great tit (*Parus major*)		3	12	16	73	82
Tree-creeper (*Certhia familiaris*)			2	4	18	76
Green woodpecker (*Picus viridis*)				4	27	71

where S is the number of species and A is the area of the island. In this case A is the area of the wood (in square metres) and the constants C and K had values of 0.55 and 0.27 respectively.

1. Draw a graph summarising the relationship between the size of a wood and the probability of finding each species within it.

2. Use your knowledge of the biology of each species to explain the pattern of distribution in woods of different sizes.

3. How many species would you expect to find in a wood of area 1 ha?

4. How many times larger must a wood be to hold exactly double this number of species?

5. Several recent Ministry of Agriculture, Fisheries and Food (MAFF) schemes have encouraged farmers in Britain to take arable land out of production and plant broad-leaved woodland. It is expected that these 'farm woodlands' would help in the conservation, among other things, of woodland birds. On the basis of the information you have been given do you think that farmers should be encouraged to plant many small woods or a single large one? Do you think the scheme will prove a successful conservation tool?

Problem 8.3	Designing a research programme on the ecological impacts of a smelter

Background When designing a programme of research, several specific questions need to be answered – about what you intend to do and why, how you will do it, and when, and how you will monitor your progress. Applications for support for research must provide that information. There are no 'right answers', but your application must show convincingly that the work is important, and will be carried out efficiently. The problem which follows is both fictitious and slightly artificial: you normally have to include the background to the project and a statement of costs (including staff whom you intend to employ) – these are not required here.

Keep the purpose firmly in mind. The final report may contain recommendations (to remove or ameliorate pollution problems), and you may be tempted to propose studies of how the organisms deal with their heavy-metal (HM) burden, but those are not the purpose of this research, which is to see what the ecological impacts are.

If you propose too many things, they will be rushed and done poorly. Instead, choose fewer things so they can be done well with sufficient replicates. Be especially wary of the effects of multiplication: for example, a sample every 1 km on a 16×16 km grid, every month, analysing for four different metals, is $17 \times 17 \times 4 \times 12 = 13\,872$ analyses in a year – that is, 38 every day for a year, and research assistants are traditionally allowed to take Christmas Day off! Also remember to allow sufficient time to get a technique working, to analyse results and to prepare the report.

Follow up this problem by writing a research proposal for a smaller project which you would like to carry out, and present it to your tutor for appraisal. Choose an area which will enhance our understanding of an aspect of environmental biology, and base it on a specific model system.

Further reading

Martin and Coughtrey (1982).

Data and question

Design a 2-year research programme to study the ecological impact of an operational zinc smelting plant (see map, Fig. 8.2).

Describe (1) the objectives, (2) the programme of work, (3) the techniques to be used, (4) your choice of specialist staff who would be engaged to assist, and include (5) a timetable showing the criteria of progress after 12 and 24 months.

The programme will start in October, and employ three research assistants, a research technician and a secretary. In addition to normal laboratory facilities and field surveying equipment, you have access to a scientific library, experimental marine and

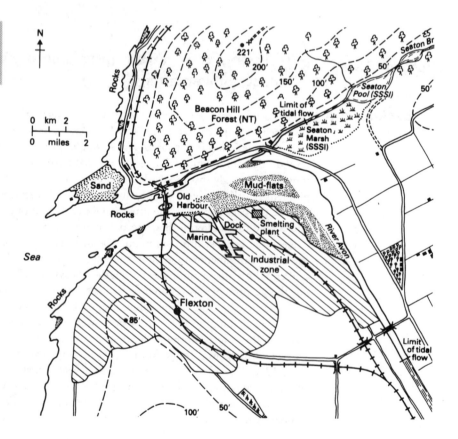

Figure 8.2. Map of the area around Flexton smelting plant.

freshwater aquaria, atomic absorption spectroscopy capable of detecting 0.1 ppm of heavy metals, and experimental grounds for the rearing of plants. A hydrological survey of the estuary and surrounding coast was carried out recently when the marina was constructed, and Flexton College has extensive records of the fauna and flora of the coasts and estuary. Flexton Natural History Society has records for Seaton Pool SSSI (site of special scientific interest) waters, marsh and woodland, and the National Trust carried out a floristic survey of Beacon Hill Forest 10 years ago.

The smelting plant chiefly processes metal ores for the extraction of zinc. Ores arrive at a new dock in the harbour, and products are transported out by rail. The chief pollutants are airborne dust containing zinc, copper, cadmium and lead, and there has been occasional contamination of water via the new dock. The prevailing wind is from the south-west. The annual rainfall is 90 cm.

The town of Flexton is an old fishing harbour, but the fishing fleet has declined, and the coastal fishery is small, except for a flourishing shellfish collection (crabs, prawns, mussels, winkles and some cockles). There is a new marina for pleasure craft, and the town now relies on tourism and mixed industry (including the smelter). The former meandering route of the River Avon was canalised over 100 years ago, and its former flat and low-lying flood plain now provides good farmland for dairying and crops (mainly wheat and potatoes, with some apple orchards). The river follows its original route from 5 km upstream of the smelter, and the mud-flats have a good covering of *Zostera* (eelgrass), supporting nationally important numbers of waders and migrating wildfowl. Most of the scenic and natural history interest lies to the north, from the rocky coast with sandy stretches, to the deciduous forest of Beacon Hill, owned by the National Trust, and the marshes and pools of Seaton Brook. The marshes and pools are a haven for birds and insects, and there is a heronry on the steep-sided wooded northern slopes of the brook. South of the town the country is a dull mixture of new plantations and sheep grazing on thin rather acid soils.

Problem 8.4 — Impact assessment of an opencast coal mine

Background
Environmental impact assessment (EIA, or just EA) is an important procedure which ensures that the possible environmental effects of new developments are fully understood and taken into account before the project is allowed to go ahead. Some projects, such as a waste disposal plant for incinerating special waste, always require EA, whereas others, such as opencast mining, require an EA only if the environmental effects are likely to be significant – as might be the case for a large project, one in a sensitive location, or one likely to produce pollutants.

Information about possible environmental effects are collected and analysed by the developer and others in order to produce an environmental statement from which the planning authority can assess the project. In addition to describing the development, the statement must include all the data necessary to identify and assess the main probable environmental effects, together with a description of those likely effects, and the scope for mitigating actions to avoid, reduce or remedy adverse effects. The environmental statement must specifically refer to the possible impact on: human

Opencast mining operations near Bolton, England. Coal is stripped from seams just beneath the surface and the spoil is back-filled.

beings, flora, fauna, soil, water, air, climate, landscape, interaction between any of the above, material assets, cultural heritage.

Further reading

Department of the Environment (1989), British Coal (1992).

Data and questions

This problem concerns a hypothetical proposed opencast coal mining operation (see Fig. 8.3). A large coal field lies near the surface and the proposal is to scrape off the soil, subsoil and overburden in order to extract coal to a maximum depth of 70 m; the soil, subsoil and overburden would be placed in separate heaps and returned after extraction. The field is in three parts, A, B and C, separated by roads. The richest seams occur in site A. Blasting would be necessary only in the western end of site C.

Table 8.3 shows the coal lying under each site. To operate profitably, at least 70 per cent of the coal must be mined. If all sites were exploited, the work would start in site A, move on to site B while A is restored, then work site C while B is restored, and finally restore site C. Each phase would last 3 years. A 5-year period of aftercare would be enforced in each site.

The land is fairly flat and of medium agricultural grade, suitable for grazing, apart from 10 per cent of derelict land, with no useful soils. There is a ruined thirteenth-century priory in site C, and part of a large deciduous woodland. There are no other woods on the sites, but the hedgerows support some bird life. In site A, and west of it, is an area containing 100 ponds, many with several species of amphibian, including the great crested newt, which is a protected species, and a rich flora, including water soldier and other species which are rare regionally and nationally. Protection of a

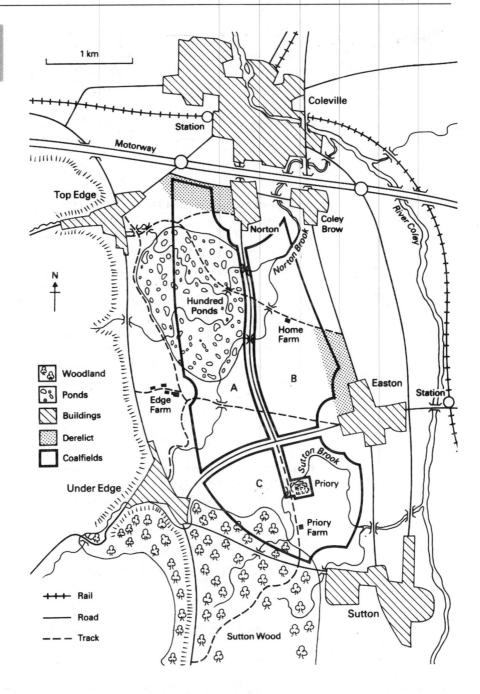

Figure 8.3. Map of the opencast coal field.

1 km

Coleville

Station

Motorway

Top Edge

Norton

Coley Brow

Norton Brook

River Coley

N

Hundred Ponds

Home Farm

A

B

Easton

Station

Woodland

Ponds

Buildings

Derelict

Coalfields

Edge Farm

Sutton Brook

Under Edge

C

Priory

Priory Farm

Sutton

Rail

Road

Track

Sutton Wood

	Site A	Site B	Site C
Area (ha)	300	200	200
% Derelict	5	5	0
% Pond area	50	0	0
% Woodland	0	0	10
Million tonnes coal	2.6	0.7	0.7

species on schedule 5 of the 1981 Wildlife and Countryside Act makes it an offence to intentionally kill, take or disturb the animal, or to damage, destroy or obstruct access to any structure or place used for shelter or protection. Pipistrelle bats, also a protected species, have roosted in Home Farm in the past. There are no reserves or SSSIs in the area, but the woodland and the area of 100 ponds are registered as sites of biological interest, although this confers no protected status on them.

To transport the coal to the railway goods station at Coleville on existing roads, wagons must pass through villages. Villages close to the proposed workings must be protected by a 200 m zone, and a 5 m high grassed bank. Two farmhouses, Priory and Home farms, of little architectural interest, would be destroyed. Roads on the site would be replaced afterwards, and streams would be diverted into settlement lagoons. Electricity, water and gas supply lines skirt around the coal field, except for supplies to Home and Priory farms.

1. Describe a route for transport of coal from the site to the goods station at Coleville which has least adverse effects.

2. List at least 20 environmental impacts resulting from the operations of (I) soil stripping and removal of overburden, (II) excavation of coal, (III) transport of coal from the sites and (IV) restoration, if all sites were fully exploited. List the four operations across the page and the impacts down the page. Describe each impact as a benefit (B), a cost (C) or neutral (–). Indicate by asterisks those adverse effects for which some mitigating action could be taken.

3. List the mitigation measures which could be taken to avoid, reduce or remedy the adverse effects.

4. Bearing in mind the possible mitigation measures and need for the operation to be profitable, which site or combination of sites should be mined?

Problem 8.5

Economic analysis of options for a geothermal power plant

Background How can you put a value on an environmental resource, or calculate the cost an environmental impact? There are, in fact, a number of ways. You could, for example, ask people how much they would be prepared to pay for admission to a reserve, or how much they spent on travelling to it. The prices of houses in rural areas might be a measure of the value of a rural landscape. In the case of environmental pollution, you might be able to calculate the economic loss suffered by a resource such as a fishery, or the cost of cleaning buildings soiled by pollution. Alternatively, you could use the cost of removing the pollutant at its source. Even if the environmental loss cannot be quantified, it can still be taken into account alongside quantifiable costs, when considering the options of a proposed development.

Further reading

Dixon *et al.* (1986).

Data and questions

In order to reduce its dependence on imported crude oil, the Philippines has considered various forms of domestic energy production, including the exploitation of a geothermal field. The geothermal power plant would produce a mix of steam and water. The major environmental effects would come from the non-extracted heat and the relatively large amounts of dissolved solids including chloride, silica, arsenic, boron and lithium in the waste water. The last three have known toxic effects on plants, animals and people, and their concentrations exceed the limits set by the National Pollution Control Commission. The severity of the effects would depend on the rate and frequency of discharge and the method of disposal.

Seven options for the disposal of the wastes were considered (Fig. 8.4):

1. Reinjection into aquifers.
2. Discharge to Mahiao river untreated.

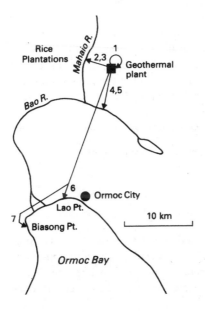

Figure 8.4. Map of the areas surrounding proposed geothermal power plant in Tongonan, Philippines.

3. Discharge to Mahiao river after removal of arsenic.
4. Discharge to Bao river untreated.
5. Discharge to Bao river after removal of arsenic.
6. Discharge untreated at sea at Lao Point.
7. Discharge untreated at sea at Biasong Point.

Option 1 includes a stand-by system of ponds used when the reinjection system is shut down temporarily for maintenance. Options 2–5 include temporary storage ponds to cool the water before discharge.

Three types of cost were calculated for each disposal option:

1. the capital cost of constructing the waste disposal plant.
2. the operating costs over a life of 30 years.
3. the environmental costs where these could be calculated. Environmental costs which cannot be calculated can still be considered in choosing one of the options.

The project has an expected life span of 30 years, but costs are expressed as present costs, by using a discount rate of 15 per cent. The choice of a particular discount rate is beyond the scope of this book, but in practice a discount rate of 15 per cent over 30 years just means multiplying the costs in each year by a given figure (0.8696 for year 1, 0.7561 for year 2, 4.9405 for all of years 3 to 30). [These figures are calculated as in the following example. If the construction costs for an option are P107m (107 million pesos) over the first 2 years of the project, this is P53.5m each year, but in year 1 the present day value of P53.5m is

$$P53.5m/(1 + 0.15)^1 = P53.5m \times 0.8696 = P46.5m$$

in year 2 it is

$$P53.5m/(1 + 0.15)^2 = P53.5m \times 0.7561 = P40.4m$$

Thus the present value of construction is P46.5m + P40.4m = P86.9m. Similarly, if the running costs for each of the 30 years apart from the first 2 years (there are no operating costs before it is built!) are P10.4m each year, the present-day cost is $P10.4m/(1 + 0.15)^3$ for the third year, plus $P10.4m/(1 + 0.15)^4$ for the fourth year and so on up to $P10.4m/(1 + 0.15)^{30}$ for the thirtieth year – this in fact totals P10.4m × 4.9405 = P51.4m. Thus the present value of the costs of constructing and running the option is P86.9m + P51.4m = P138.3m.]

Costs and environmental effects of the seven waste disposal options

Only the costs of each waste disposal option are given, not the capital and running costs of the power plant itself.

Option 1 (Reinjection)

The construction would cost P107m over 2 years. Annual operating costs would be P10.4m. Although the most ecologically sound method, reinjection into the aquifers might lower the temperature and hence the energy extracted. There are no measurable environmental costs, and the direct costs of construction and operating are calculated as follows to be P138.3m:

	Million P
Construction (spread over years 1 and 2)	
Reinjection wells	70
Pipeline	20
Stand-by system	17
	107
Construction cost per year (=107/2)	53.5
Operating costs per year for years 3–30	10.4

Cash flow

Year	1	2	3	...	30
Million P	53.5	53.5	10.4		10.4

Present value at 15% discount rate

Year 1	53.5 × 0.8696	46.5
Year 2	53.5 × 0.7561	40.4
Years 3–30	10.4 × 4.9405	51.4
Present value of total direct cost		138.3

Option 2 (Discharge to Mahiao river untreated)

The risk to human health and livestock will be removed by building a water-purification plant in years 1 and 2, costing P50m. to construct and P15m annually to operate and maintain. A cooling pond and pipelines would be built in year 2 at a cost of P7m. Yearly running costs would be P0.0433m.

When the system is operational (years 3 to 30), further environmental costs would result from high levels of arsenic and boron in untreated wastes discharged to the river which would lower the productivity of 4000 ha of rice fields. If the irrigation water is heavily polluted, farmers would not irrigate, with a heavy loss of production – irrigated rice fields yield 3050 kg ha^{-1} and two crops per year are possible, while unirrigated fields yield 1895 kg ha^{-1} and only produce one crop per year. The net return for irrigated rice is P346 per Ha, and P324 ha^{-1} for unirrigated rice.

Another environmental cost is the pollution of the delta, affecting important marine fisheries. The net return from these is estimated at 29 per cent of the value of the catch, which is typically P39.4m year^{-1}.

The environmental cost to the freshwater ecosystem cannot be estimated, because the value of fishing in the river is unknown.

Option 3 (Discharge to Mahiao river after removal of arsenic)

A cooling pond and pipelines would be built, and arsenic removed at the well-heads. The effects of the remaining boron on rice production and aquatic ecosystems are unknown, but a water purification plant would be built.

Option 4 (Discharge to Bao river untreated)

A cooling pond and pipelines would be built, and the waste water discharged below the rice fields. A water purification plant would be built for the residents along the lower reaches of the Bao River. The costs to the marine fishery are the same as in option 2.

Option 5 (Discharge to Bao river after removal of arsenic)

As in option 4, but arsenic removal would increase costs, although the water purification plant will be cheaper than in option 4, because arsenic treatment is already removed.

Option 6 (Discharge untreated at sea at Lao Point)

A 22 km pipeline would be built. The cost of affected marine productivity cannot be estimated.

Option 7 (Discharge untreated at sea at Biasong Point)

A 32 km pipeline would be built. The cost of affected marine productivity cannot be estimated.

The total direct costs of options 1–7 estimated so far are given in Table 8.4.

	Option	Direct cost	Environmental cost	Total measured cost	Non-quantifiable or non-measured costs
Table 8.4. Costs of waste disposal under the seven options (million P).	1	138.3	Unknown	138.3	Energy loss
	2	?	Rice? Sea fishery?	?	Freshwater fishery livestock health, laundry, bathing, human health, marine ecosystems
	3	359.3		359.3	Rice production, lower losses than in option 2 except marine ecosystems
	4	81.1	Sea fishery?	?	Freshwater fishery livestock health, laundry, bathing, human health, marine ecosystems
	5	359.1		359.1	Less than option 4
	6	243.1	Unknown	243.1	High
	7	353.3	Unknown	353.3	High

1. In option 2, calculate the annual loss if irrigation water was unusable for the whole 4000 ha.

2. Express this loss as the present day value of rice loss over years 3–30 using a 15 per cent discount rate.

3. Calculate the annual economic loss to the marine fishery in option 2 if HM contamination occurs.

4. Express this loss as the present day value of fishery loss over years 3–30, using a 15 per cent discount rate.

5. Calculate the present day value of the total direct costs of construction and operation of option 2, using a 15 per cent discount rate.

6. Table 8.4 compares the costs of waste disposal under the seven alternative schemes. Insert your calculated values of the direct costs of option 2, and the environmental costs to rice production in option 2 and to sea fisheries in options 2 and 4 into the table, and then calculate the missing values for total measured costs for options 2 and 4.

7. From the now complete version of Table 8.4, analyse the options, to choose the most preferred one.

SOLUTIONS

Problem 8.1   The reserve can be divided into seven areas for management (A to G in Fig. 8.5). The notes referred to for habitat assessment are in the box on pp. 141–143.

Area A   1. Habitat: Patch of gorse below observation tower.
2. Assessment: Valuable habitat for resident and migrant birds (note 1).
3. Management objectives: Retain, and if possible increase diversity. Keep verges tidy.
4. Management prescription: Trim verge and glade edges annually. Contain rosebay. Plant native berry-bearing trees, as food for birds.
5. Priority: 2.
6. Time-scale: Continuous low-level maintenance each year.

Area B   1. Habitat: Pylon bank path.
2. Assessment: Young woodland area, with valuable collection of planted willows; useful food-plants for butterflies and their caterpillars (notes 2 and 3). Noise and visual intrusion from main road.

Figure 8.5. Map of Heysham Nature Reserve, showing separate habitat areas considered in the management prescription.

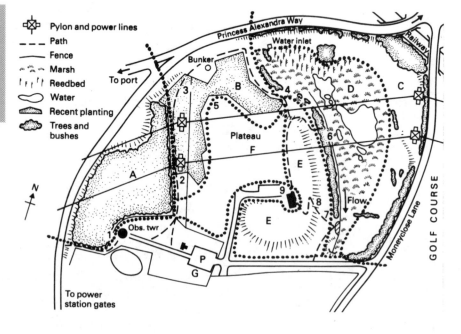

3. Management objectives: Maintain willow collection. Maintain food-plants. Plant hedge to screen from road.
4. Management prescription: Prevent undergrowth smothering willows, and thin out as necessary. Label individual trees. Control aggressive weeds: avoid fertilisers. Plant thorn hedge (blackthorn/sea buckthorn as alternative to hawthorn) with mixture of native trees.
5. Priority: 1.
6. Time-scale: Tree labels and thorn hedge in year 1. Weed control annually.

Area C
1. Habitat: NE boundary banks.
2. Assessment: Not on route, so no notes, but steeply sloping with tree and hedge screen, and open grassland down to marsh. Probably a valuable refuge for shier species. Build-up of dead undergrowth is possible fire risk. Possible runoff of nutrients across this area.
3. Management objectives: Maintain scrubs and trees as refuge for shier species. Reduce fire risk. Retain privacy. Investigate and, if necessary, control nutrient runoff.
4. Management prescription: Coppice trees and pile some dead wood as refugia for invertebrates. Remove dead undergrowth. Retain privacy by polite notices on paths requesting vistors not to venture on to this area, and saying why.

   Analyse runoff water collected by digging short trench beside lane. If results of analysis justify it, extend trench along lane to carry runoff into stream where it exits the reserve. If no nutrifying runoff detected, reroute stream through open water to reduce residence time.
5. Priority: 2.
6. Time-scale: Clear undergrowth annually after seed set in autumn; coppice half now, other half in 3–5 years. Place notices in year 1 and maintain annually. Dig experimental trench in year 1.

Area D
1. Habitat: marsh and stream.
2. Assessment: See notes 4, 6 and 7. Valuable open water and marsh, for birds, dragonflies etc. and visually. Reeds and reedmace encroaching open water rapidly.
3. Management objectives: Maintain reedbeds and extend open water. Maintain willow screen and observation platform. Maintain stream and dipping pond, for increased educational use.
4. Management prescription: Silting up and invasion of open water by marginal plants must be tackled by hand (because machinery prohibited from working under power lines) in winter (to avoid disturbance to nesting birds). Area of open water to be doubled. Control water levels with sluice. Maintain willow screen, viewing platform and paths to platform and to dipping well to prevent visitors trampling vegetation on sides. Cut back trees shading pond area.
5. Priority: 1.
6. Time-scale: Excavation of open water in year 1 (and 2 if necessary). Maintain paths annually.

Area E 1. Habitat: grassy banks in front of classroom.
2. Assessment: Many flowers and food-plants of butterflies. See note 8.
3. Management objectives: Maintain diversity of flora and fauna.
4. Management prescription: Mow in autumn after seed set, and remove mowings.
5. Priority: 2.
6. Time-scale: Annually.

Area F 1. Habitat: plateau behind classroom.
2. Assessment: Low, thin grass with herbs overlying basic rubble and PFA, some rubble piles used for invertebrate refugia (notes 9 and 5). Currently low value. Potential for educational use.
3. Management objectives: Retain refugia. Improve educational value.
4. Management prescription: Retain and extend refugia stones. Strip back soil layer on one-third of plot now, another in 5 years, final one-third in 10 years to study recolonisation (avoid harsh straight edges to strips).
5. Priority: 3.
6. Time-scale: Years 1, 5, 10.

Area G 1. Habitat: roads, paths, carpark, buildings, boundaries.
2. Assessment: Essential for visitor access for recreation and education. Potential for vandalism, motor cycling and fly-tipping.
3. Management objectives: Improve access for disabled. Discourage vandalism and fly-tipping. Improve facilities for educational use. Improve facilities for recreational visitors. Maintain boundary fences.
4. Management prescription: Graded ramp from power station entrance, and major paths suitable for wheelchairs. Log kerbs to roads to prevent vehicles going off road. Skip placed near entrance to Moneyclose Lane by local council? Road gates to entrance locked at sunset, then entry and exit by pedestrian gate.
    Replace 'notes' by informative signs, and sign route through reserve. Explanatory signs at entrances.
    Maintain classroom and other buildings. Fit shutters to windows. Maintain boundary fences and keep vegetation along edges tidy.
5. Priority: 2.
6. Timescale: Continuous.

Whole reserve 1. Assessment: Pleasant mix of typical habitats with a high degree of naturalness, offering space for a variety of birds, insects and herbs, as well as recreational and educational use.
2. Management objectives: Retain habitats, reducing encroachment of open water. Encourage species diversity. Increase educational value. Keep outer edges looking cared-for, and increase environmental interpretation signs.
3. Management prescription: As detailed in individual sections.

Problem 8.2

1. The relationship between size of wood and the probability of finding each species of passerine within it is shown in Fig. 8.6.

2. Most of the species are more frequently encountered in larger woods. The probability that blackbirds are found in woods increases steadily as the size of the wood increases and all very large woods contain blackbirds. However, blackbirds are found even in woods too tiny to support a territory. This tells us that blackbirds survive well in woods but do not necessarily need woodland, as they can also survive elsewhere. With their broad diet, which consists of a mixture of fruit and invertebrates, blackbirds can feed both in woods and in open country, though they will nest in trees. Great tits, in contrast, are found only in woods greater than 0.01 ha and are only common in woods of over 10 ha. This shows that these birds are more dependent on woodland, probably for their food which consists largely of seeds. Tree-creepers and green woodpeckers require still greater areas of woodland, probably because of their diet. Tree-creepers eat insects and other invertebrates which hide in bark and which become scarce in winter. Woodpeckers live on an even more specialised diet of insect larvae obtained from rotten wood; a larger area of woodland will be required to provide an adequate supply of this sort of food for this large bird.

   In contrast to all the other species, house sparrows are encountered less frequently in very large woods than small ones. This tells us that the house sparrow is not a woodland species, though it may occasionally obtain food and shelter from the woodland edge. Instead, it is a bird of open country, where it feeds on the seeds of grasses and other herbs, or towns, where it feeds on cheese and pickle sandwiches.

3. The number of species in a wood of 1 ha can be calculated from equation (1).

$$\text{Number} = 0.55 \times (10^4)^{0.27} = 6.6 \text{ species}$$

Figure 8.6. The relationship between the size of woods and the proportion which contain particular species of birds.

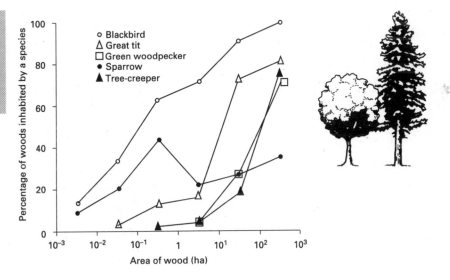

4. To hold double the number of species (13.2) the wood must be larger. Using equation (1),

$$13.2 = 0.55 \times (A)^{0.27}$$

$$A^{0.27} = 24.0$$

$$A = 24.0^{1/0.27}$$

$$= 1.29 \times 10^5 \ m^2$$

This area equals 12.9 ha, 12.9 times as large.

5. Planting lots of small woods would encourage a few species of birds, such as blackbirds and great tits. However, these species are already common and blackbirds are not strictly woodland birds. It would be better to plant a few large woods which provide habitat for more species, including such entirely woodland birds as tree-creepers and green woodpeckers. The problem with the farm woodland scheme is that because most farms are from 50 to 500 ha in size and because farmers would be unwilling to plant woodland on more than a small fraction of their land, most woods created would be relatively small. True woodland birds would not therefore be encouraged.

Problem 8.3

Preparatory notes
1. Decide what you want to achieve by the end of 2 years (the objectives).

2. List available techniques.

3. Review what is already known (and reject irrelevant information), and how you need to build on this.

4. List any major constraints.
   (a) Smelter is operational, so before-and-after comparisons are impossible. However, comparisons might be made between sites nearer and further from source.
   (b) Seasons: animals and plants not available all year round. The work starts in October, when plenty of biomass could be collected for analysis, and desk studies made through winter.
   (c) Time: final report required 2 years from start.

5. Divide problem into sections (e.g. marine, freshwater, land) and list the things to do in each *which lead to the goal* – i.e. which show effects of the smelter on ecology; this means more than just describing levels of pollutants. Effects on farming, urban areas and humans are only obliquely *ecological* impacts.

6. Prioritise. Which of all the ideas in item 4 will most likely and most rapidly lead to the desired end result? Several things may have equal priority. Most of the above stages are shown in the 'brain-storming' spider-diagram in Fig. 8.7.

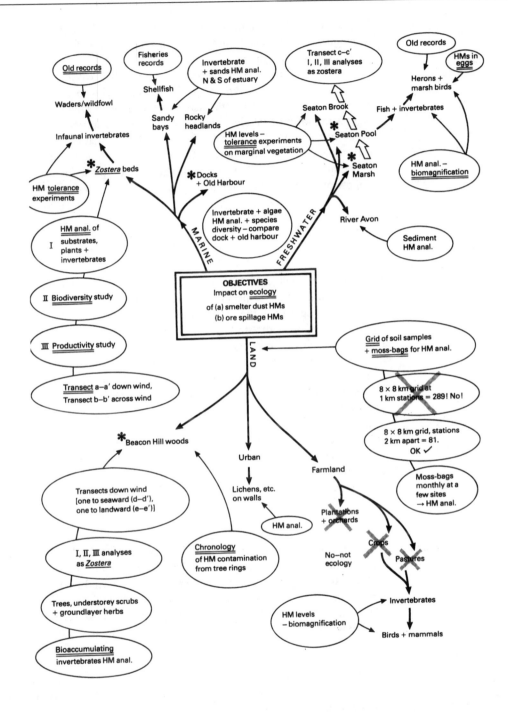

Figure 8.7. 'Spider diagram' – the result of brainstorming ideas for the research programme to study ecological impacts of a smelter. From the objectives box (centre), three major strands radiate, with each successively subdivided. Priority items are asterisked. Techniques to be employed on each aspect are ringed. Key words underlined. Two ideas are crossed out – one because it is unfeasible, the other because it does not pursue the objectives. (HM anal = heavy metal analysis by atomic absorption spectroscopy for zinc, copper, cadmium and lead.)

7. Prepare the information, in the format requested (objectives, programme, techniques, staff, timetable and criteria of progress), clearly and succinctly, giving reasons for your decisions.

Because there are several high-priority areas, they will be done concurrently. This, together with the type of work required, helps to determine the type of research personnel and the timetable to be adopted. Divide the timetable into eight 3-month seasonal blocks for each of the three habitats. Decide what you can do in the time, when is the best time for each and what must be done first. Alter earlier ideas. Allow sufficient time for developing techniques, analysing results and preparing the report. Read through the final proposal to make sure that the important points are prominent.

A specimen answer:

Objectives   The programme will describe the ecological impacts on marine, freshwater and terrestrial communities, of heavy metal (HM) discharge in airborne dust from the smelter and ore spillage in the old harbour. Because the extent of HM contamination is not reliably known, the study will determine the levels of HM in organisms and substrates, as well as comparing the species composition of each of the communities with similar ones further away, and investigating responses of individual organisms (tolerance, changes in size and fecundity) to the HM burdens, including experiments to determine the uptake, loss and sequestration of HMs.

Priority will be given to the most sensitive communities – the *Zostera* beds on the estuary mud-flats which support important populations of waders and migrating wildfowl, Seaton Marsh and Pool SSSI, and Beacon Hill deciduous woodlands, and the surrounding rocky and sandy shores which support recreation and shellfish collection. The effects on ecological communities in the town and harbour, and on wildlife and flora of neighbouring farmland will also be considered.

Programme   1. The marine study will start with a determination of the levels of zinc, copper, cadmium and lead in plants, infaunal invertebrates and substrate samples of the *Zostera* beds, collected along a transect (a–a') downwind from the smelter across the estuary (see Fig. 8.8). A second transect (b–b') would be made along the river (including the channel to the old harbour) to access the width of the fallout plume and possible water-borne pollution from ore handling in the old harbour. As well as a complete species composition, the size and abundance of organisms would be recorded at each sampling station.

The rates of uptake, loss and sequestration of HMs by plants and infaunal invertebrates on the *Zostera* beds would be determined in the laboratory to assess the potential for recovery.

The levels of HM in sediments and the faunal composition in the old harbour near the quay used for handling ore would be compared with those in a section which the ore ships do not use.

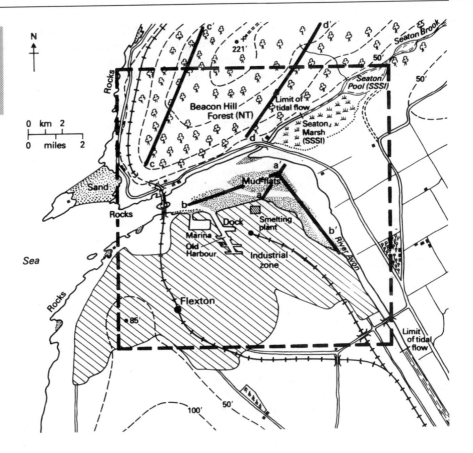

Faunal composition, abundance and sizes of individual animals would be determined on rocky and sandy shores to the north and south of the estuary, and HM concentrations of invertebrates and substrates recorded.

Wading bird population records would be examined to ascertain whether these have declined in recent years, compared to records elsewhere.

2. Seaton Pool SSSI ponds and marshes lie close downwind of the smelter, so we would concentrate the freshwater work here. Levels of HM in sediments, plants and aquatic fauna would be sampled from the mouth of the brook towards the north-east until HM levels fall to background intensity. Species diversity and productivity would be mapped. The tolerance to and additive effects of HM on aquatic vegetation collected near to and far from the smelter would be assessed by germination and growth experiments in containers of different concentrations and mixtures of zinc, copper, cadmium and lead.

3. *Sphagnum* moss bags would be placed at 2 km intervals on land lying within a grid 16 × 16 km centred on the smelter to monitor airborne fallout (Fig. 8.8). Soil samples would also be measured at these stations.

Beacon Hill forest, owned by the National Trust, lies downwind of the smelter on high ground. This important site is therefore at risk. Levels of HMs in leaves of trees, scrubs and groundlayer herbs and in soil would be determined along two north–south transects on the seaward and landward sides. If soil levels are low, levels in earthworms and woodlice, known to bioaccumulate, would be examined. A vegetation survey in the most and least contaminated areas would compare plant species diversity and size and reproductive status of individual plants. Animal diversity and abundance would also be compared between the two sites. Heavy metal determinations from felled timber would be taken to examine the build-up of HM levels since the smelter became operational. Heavy metal levels in farmland birds and mammals from the south would be monitored.

The diversity of lichens and fauna and flora of the walls of the old town would be assessed, together with their HM levels, and compared at different locations, coincident with *Sphagnum* bag and soil-sampling sites.

Techniques used
The concentrations of zinc, copper, cadmium and lead in soil, sand and mud samples and in plants and invertebrates collected from transects and from a series of stations 2 km apart in a grid centred on the smelter, will be analysed by atomic absorption spectroscopy. *Sphagnum* moss bags will be hung at the grid stations to collect HMs each month.

The impact of HM pollution on communities will be analysed by standard species diversity sampling. Measurements will be made of individual specimens of certain species to allow impacts on growth, fecundity and productivity to be estimated.

Laboratory tests of seed germination and seedling growth rates will be made in known concentrations of HMs to detect tolerance, and in mixtures of different HMs to determine cross-tolerance and additive effects of HMs.

Attempts will be made to match the chronology of HM pollution with the operation of the smelter using substrate samples from different depths and in tree rings from felled timber.

Staff
Several lines would be investigated simultaneously, each requiring specialist skills. The required staff are: marine research assistant, freshwater research assistant, terrestrial research assistant, secretary with library skills, technician skilled in HM analysis. All research assistants would be skilled in identification and field sampling techniques.

Timetable
In year 1, the moss-bag and soil sample determinations of HMs from the 16 km grid on the land would be completed. The investigations of HM loads in the *Zostera* beds, the old harbour and Seaton Brook SSSI would be completed, together with the faunistic surveys of the old harbour, and floristic surveys of Seaton Brook. The vegetation survey of Beacon Hill forest, together with HM analyses of forest plants and invertebrates, would be completed.

In year 2, the ecological surveys of *Zostera* beds and sandy and rocky shores to north and south of the estuary would be completed. The results would be collated with published fisheries and shellfish catches and old records of shore communities. Seaton Brook SSSI faunistic samples would be completed, and aquatic plants grown in containers to establish tolerance to and interactions of HMs. The detailed survey of productivity and biodiversity in the least and most affected areas of woodland on Beacon Hill would be completed, as would the study of species diversity and HM levels of lichens and other plants and invertebrates on walls in the urban areas. Determination of HM levels in woodland and farmland birds and mammals would be concluded. The chronological study of HM pollution would be completed.

Problem 8.4

1. An exit from the northern edge of site A on to the road between Norton and Top Edge should be created, controlled by traffic lights, to enable lorries to cross the motorway along the Top Edge to Colville road. The turning on to the Top Edge to Coleville road may need widening.

2. The impacts of the mining operations are shown in Table 8.5.

3. The adverse environmental impacts of the opencast mining operations identified in Table 8.5 could be mitigated by the following actions (numbers refer to impact factors from table):

   1. Noise. Place topsoil in 5 m high banks as sound baffles between site and nearby dwellings. Ban night working. Prohibit site traffic through villages or town.
   2. Blasting. Restrict number each day. Ban weekend blasting.
   3. Damage to dwellings by site traffic. Route traffic away from villages.
   5. Mud on roads. Wash lorry wheels before leaving site.
   8+11. Destruction of pond flora and fauna. Establish conservation area in pond area off the mining site. Remove plants and amphibia to existing and new ponds on conservation area. Re-establish pond area during restoration and replace flora and fauna.
   10+13. Destruction of hedgerows. Replant hedgerows during restoration.
   14. Loss of topsoil. Store in separate mounds and respread during restoration.
   16. Dust. Spray site tracks in dry weather. Cease operations on site in dry, windy weather. Vegetate mounds. Wash lorry wheels before leaving site.
   17+18. Contamination and disruption of watercourses. Divert streams flowing into sites and dig trench to collect runoff from site into settlement lagoons before returning water to streams flowing from site.
   19. Visual impact of mounds.
      (a) Place overburden mounds away from dwellings.
      (b) Limit height.
      (c) Backfill immediately after extraction of coal.
      (d) Screen site with grassed 5 m topsoil banks 200 m from dwellings.
      (e) Plant fast-growing trees in front of banks.
   20. Visual impact of pits. As 19(c), (d) and (e). Also prevent excavation and coaling work taking place on all sites simultaneously.
   21. Erosion. Seed mounds with grass.

Table 8.5. Impacts of mining operations.	Operation			
Impacts on:	I	II	III	IV
Humans				
1 Noise of machines, lorries	C★	C★	C★	C★
2 Noise of blasting	C★	–	–	–
3 Damage to dwellings by traffic	–	–	C★	–
4 Traffic delays	C	C	C	C
5 Mud on roads	–	–	C★	C★
6 Employment	B	B	B	B
7 Creation of recreation space	–	–	–	B
Flora				
8 Destruction of ponds	C★	–	–	–
9 Destruction of woodland	C	–	–	–
10 Destruction of hedgerows	C★	–	–	–
Fauna				
11 Destruction of ponds (amphibia)	C★	–	–	–
12 Destruction of woodland	C	–	–	–
13 Destruction of hedgerows (birds)	C★	–	–	–
Soil				
14 Loss of topsoil	C★	–	–	–
15 Replacement of derelict land	–	–	B	B
Air				
16 Dust	C★	–	C★	C★
Water				
17 Contamination	C★	C★	–	–
18 Disruption of flow	C★	–	–	–
	–	–	–	–
Climate	–	–	–	–
Landscape				
19 Soil and overburden mounds	C★	–	–	–
20 Pits in ground	C★	C★	–	–
Interactions				
21 Erosion of mounds contaminating/blocking waterways	C★	–	–	–
Material assets				
22 Loss of farmsteads	C	–	–	–
Cultural heritage				
23 Loss of ancient priory	C	–	–	–

Note: Operations: I = removal of soil and overburden, II = excavation of coal, III = transport of coal from site, IV = restoration. B = benefit, C = cost, C★ = cost but mitigation possible.

4. If all sites are mined fully, the total coal extracted is 2.6 + 0.7 + 0.7 = 4 million t. The operation must extract 70 per cent of this to be profitable, i.e. 3 million t. Site A alone provides 2.6 million t, sites B and C 0.7 million t apiece. Mining any one site, or only B and C are therefore non-viable options. Viable options are thus A + B + C (4 million t), A + B or A + C (3.3 million t each).

Consider now the environmental impacts of these three options. If A + B + C are mined excluding the pond area the yield is 1.3 + 0.7 + 0.7 = 2.7 million t, again non-viable. If A + B + C excluding the woodland is mined the yield is 3.93 million t, and so the destruction of the woodland is difficult to justify – it would take several decades to replace. The pipistrelle bats can be discounted – you cannot conserve what is not there – so area B can be included, and there is then the opportunity to return derelict land on B to use. Since a reasonable mitigation measure to deal with the impact on the pond area has been proposed, this option offers greatest profitability with least environmental loss.

Thus mining A + B + C, excluding the woodland in C but including the ponds area in A and taking mitigating action, emerges as an acceptable option.

Problem 8.5

1. Calculation of annual loss from rice production if irrigation was unusable for the whole 4000 ha.

    With irrigation: 4000 ha × P346 ha^{-1} × 2 crops = P2.768m.
    No irrigation: 4000 ha × P324 ha^{-1} × 1 crop = P1.296m.

    Therefore, annual loss to rice crop = P2.768m − P1.296m = P1.47m

2. The present day value of rice loss over years 3–30 using a 15 per cent discount rate is P1.47m × 4.9405 = P7.26m.

3. Annual loss to marine fisheries = P39.4m × 0.29 = P11.4m.

4. The present day value of fishery loss over years 3–30, using a 15 per cent discount rate, is P11.4m × 4.9405 = P56.3m.

5. Calculation of direct costs of option 2, discounted at 15 per cent per year.

	Million P
Construction	
Cooling pond and piplines (built in year 2)	7
Water purification system (built in years 1 and 2)	50
	—
Operating costs per year	
Cooling pond	0.0433
Water purification system	15.0

Cash flow					
Year	1	2	3	...	30
Water purification	25	25	15		15
Cooling pond and pipes	—	7	0.0433		0.0433
Cost in year	25	32	15.0433		15.0433

Present value at 15% discount rate		
Year 1	25 × 0.8696	21.74
Year 2	32 × 0.7561	24.20
Years 3–30	15.0433 × 4.9405	74.32
Present value of total direct cost		120.26

6. Table 8.6 is a redrawn version of Table 8.4, with the missing values inserted.

7. Without including environmental costs, option 4 (discharge of untreated wastes into the Bao river) would have been chosen because it has the lowest direct cost. However, total measurable costs allow options 3, 5, 6 and 7 to be rejected because they are relatively expensive. Options 1, 2 and 4 remain. Option 4 is the cheapest of these, but both option 4 and option 2 may cause serious marine pollution, whereas option 1 only suffers from possible loss of energy. Hence option 1 (reinjection) is the most preferred option, despite slightly higher measured costs.

Table 8.6. Redrawn Table 8.4: costs of waste disposal (million P).

Option	Direct cost	Environmental cost	Total measured cost	Non-quantifiable or non-measured costs
1	138.3	Unknown	138.3	Energy loss
2	120.2	Rice: 7.3 Sea fishery: 56.5	184.3	Freshwater fishery livestock health, laundry, bathing, human health, marine ecosystems
3	359.3		359.3	Rice production, lower losses than in option 2 except marine ecosystems
4	81.1	Sea fishery: 56.5	137.6	Freshwater fishery stock health, laundry, bathing, human health, marine ecosystems
5	359.1		359.1	Less than option 4
6	243.1	Unknown	243.1	High
7	353.3	Unknown	353.3	High

FURTHER READING

Addiscott TM, Whitmore AP and Powlson DS (1991) *Farming, Fertilizers and the Nitrate Problem*. CAB International, Wallingford.

Anderson P and Yalden DW (1981) Increased sheep numbers and the loss of heather moorland in the peak district, England. *Biological Conservation* 20, 195–213.

Atkins MD (1980) *Introduction to Insect Behaviour*. Macmillan, New York.

Barnard C, Gilbert F and McGregor P (1993) *Asking Questions in Biology: Design, Analysis and Presentation of Practical Work*. Longman, Harlow.

Batterbee RW (1984) Diatom analysis and the acidification of lakes. *Philosophical Transactions of the Royal Society of London B* 305, 451–77.

Batterbee RW, Flower RJ, Stevenson AC and Rippey B (1985) Lake acidification in Galway: a paleoecological test of competing hypotheses. *Nature* 314, 350–2.

Begon M (1979) *Investigating Animal Abundance*. Edward Arnold, London.

Begon M, Harper JL and Townsend CR (1986) *Ecology: Individuals, Populations and Communities*. Blackwell, Oxford.

Begon M and Mortimer M (1981) *Population Ecology*. Blackwell Scientific, London.

Belovsky GE (1978) Diet optimisation in a generalist herbivore: the moose. *Theoretical Population Biology* 14, 105–34.

Bransford JD and Stein BS (1984) *The Ideal Problem Solver*. WH Freeman, New York.

Briggs D and Courtney F (1989) *Agriculture and Environment: The Physical Geography of Temperate Agricultural Systems*. Longman, Harlow.

British Coal (1992) *Proposed Lomax (Revised) Opencast Coal Site Environmental Statement*. British Coal Opencast, Sheffield.

Burn AJ, Coaker TH and Jepson PC (1987) *Integrated Pest Management*. Academic Press, London.

Cadogan A and Sutton R (1994) *Maths for Advanced Biology*. Nelson, Glasgow.

Cheremisinoff NP (1978) *Fundamentals of Wind Energy*. Ann Arbor Science.

Crawley MJ (1986) *Plant Ecology*. Blackwell Scientific, Oxford.

Department of the Environment (1989) *Environmental Assessment: a Guide to the Procedures*. HMSO, London.

Dixon JA, Carpenter RA, Fallon LA, Sherman PB and Manopimoke S (1986) *Economic Analysis of the Environmental Impacts of Development Projects*. Earthscan Publications Ltd, London.

Easson DL, White EM and Pickles SJ (1993) The effects of weather, seed rate and cultivar on lodging and yield in winter wheat. *Journal of Agricultural Science* 121, 145–56.

Fitter AH and Hay RKM (1987) *Environmental Physiology of Plants (2nd edn)*. Academic Press, London.

Green B (1981) *Countryside Conservation*. Chapman and Hall, London.

Harborne JB (1988) *Introduction to Ecological Biochemistry*. Academic Press, London.

Hochachka PW and Somero, GN (1973) *Strategies of Biochemical Adaptation*. Saunders, Philadelphia.

Holland DG and Harding JPC (1984) Mersey. In B Whitton (Ed.) *Ecology of European Rivers*, pp. 113–44. Blackwell Science, Oxford.

Krebs CJ (1994) *Ecology, the Experimental Analysis of Distribution and Abundance* (4th edn). Harper International, New York.

Krebs JR and Davies NB (1993) *An Introduction to Behavioural Ecology* (3rd edn). Blackwell, Oxford.

MacArthur RH and Wilson EO (1967) *The Theory of Island Biogeography*. Princeton University Press, Princeton.

Magurran AE (1988) *Ecological Diversity and its Measurement*. Croom Helm, London.

Martin MH and Coughtrey PJ (1982) *Biological Monitoring of Heavy Metal Pollution*. Applied Science Publishers, London and New York.

Mason BJ (1992) *Acid Rain: Its Causes and Effects in Inland Waters*. Clarendon Press, Oxford.

Mason CF (1991) *Biology of Freshwater Pollution* (2nd edn). Longman, Harlow.

May RM (1985) Population dynamics: communities. In H Messel (Ed.) *The Study of Populations*, pp 31–44c. Pergamon Press, Australia.

Mellanby K (1980) *The Biology of Pollution*. Edward Arnold, London.

Miles J (1978) *Vegetation Dynamics*. Chapman & Hall, London.

Moore NW and Hooper MD (1975) On the number of bird species in British woods. *Biological Conservation* **8**, 239–50.

Morgan RPC (1986) *Soil Erosion and Conservation*. Longman, Harlow.

Park CC (1987) *Acid Rain: Rhetorics and Reality*. Routledge, London.

Peterken GF and Game M (1981) Historical factors affecting the distribution of *Mercurialis perennis* in central Lincolnshire. *Journal of Ecology* **69**, 781–96.

Phillipson J (1966) *Ecological Energetics*. Edward Arnold, London.

Rackham O (1986) *The History of the Countryside*. JM Dent, London.

Readings from *Scientific American* (1973) *Ecology, Evolution and Population Biology*. Freeman, San Francisco.

Salisbury FW and Ross CW (1992) *Plant Physiology*. Wadworth Publishing, California.

Schmidt-Nielson K (1990) *Animal Physiology: Adaptation and Environment*. Cambridge University Press, Cambridge.

Sprent JI (1987) *The Ecology of the Nitrogen Cycle*. Cambridge University Press, Cambridge.

Rundel PW (1980) The ecological distribution of C_4 and C_3 grasses in the Hawaiian Islands. *Oecologia* **45**, 354–9.

Tait J (1988) *Practical Conservation: Site Assessment and Management Planning*. The Open University, London.

Tallis JH (1991) *Plant Community History: Long Term Changes in Plant Distribution and Diversity*. Chapman & Hall, London.

Usher MB and Thompson DBA (1988) *Ecological Change in the Uplands*. Blackwell Scientific, Oxford.

Warren A and Goldsmith FB eds (1983) *Conservation in Perspective*. John Wiley, Chichester.

Watt TA (1993) *Introductory Statistics for Biology Students*. Chapman & Hall, London.

Webb N (1986) *Heathlands*. Collins, London.

Wild A (1993) *Soils and the Environment: An Introduction*. Cambridge University Press, Cambridge.

Williamson M (1981) *Island Populations*. Oxford University Press, Oxford.

INDEX